NEWTON
DEMANDS THE
MUSE

Newton's *Opticks*
and the Eighteenth Century Poets

By MARJORIE HOPE NICOLSON

PRINCETON
PRINCETON UNIVERSITY PRESS

TO

OUR COLUMBIA SECRETARIES

MARGARET BOHAN

AND

ADELE MENDELSOHN

*who "wrote" this book, as they have written
so many of our books and articles,
this study of their friend "Mr. Newton"
is affectionately dedicated
by the author*

PREFACE

APPEARANCES to the contrary notwithstanding, this volume was not deliberately begun, as it seems to have ended, as one of the various studies I have published over a period of years dealing with the impact of science upon literary imagination. Indeed I had no intention of writing this book. It insisted upon being written, and by that insistence interrupted work upon a larger volume upon which I was engaged. While reading widely in eighteenth century poetry for other purposes, I found myself constantly teased by dozens of references to Newton which had nothing to do with the *Principia*, until I became persuaded that, among the poets, the *Opticks* was even more familiar than was the more famous work. As I continued to collect references, largely to clarify my own ideas, I found the results so interesting that I proposed to the Editorial Committee of *The Journal of the History of Ideas* a paper, which was listed for some months among forthcoming articles. However, when I began serious work on the subject, I realized that the materials were so extensive and the implications so far-reaching that I could not treat them in a single paper. Hence the present version.

My original intention was to deal with all the poets of the first half-century. As I have indicated, Newton's theories of color and some of his theories of light were known before 1704, when the first edition of the *Opticks* appeared. However I found that references of poets in the early period—largely to the prism—were so few and casual that they were practically nonsignificant. While I have suggested the most interesting treatments before the death of Newton, I have purposely reduced the first section to a minimum. The great influence of Newton upon poetry began at the time of his death in 1727 in the period of "deification"; it continued almost unabated until the mid-century, when reaction began to set in. Except for Richard Jago, all the poetry considered in the main body of the study was written between 1727 and 1756-57, a terminal date which I selected because of the publication at that time of Burke's *Enquiry*. While a few rare Newtonian poems, which I know exist, proved unavailable during the war years, I think that I have read all available material, which is far more extensive than even my quotations and references indicate. Much of the poetry of tribute was dull, repetitious, uninspired. It was no part of my scheme to indicate that I had read it if it did not prove germane to my purposes.

In quoting from the poets I have, so far as proved feasible, referred to standard collections like those of Samuel Johnson and Alexander Chalmers, which are usually available. Thomson's *Seasons*, of course, requires a variorum edition; in the case of Akenside, I purposely used the first edition of *The Pleasures of Imagination*, since there are important differences between that and the revised edition. While I have used all four editions of the *Opticks* published in Newton's lifetime—1704, 1717, 1721, 1730—I have quoted from the modern Whittaker reprint of the fourth edition, the last corrected by Newton himself. However, I have given reference to sections as well as to pages in order that passages may be found by a reader of any edition of the *Opticks*.

Until this work was nearly finished I did not happen to see a brief article by Mr. Clark Emery, "Optics and Beauty" (*Modern Language Quarterly*, III [1942], pp. 45-50). I have inevitably covered the same ground, yet I trust that the larger scope of my study will justify the apparent repetition.

My thanks are due to various colleagues who may find themselves quoted without quotation marks on these pages. I offer thanks particularly to Professors Philip Wiener and John Herman Randall, Jr., who made various suggestions which I have attempted to incorporate.

Unless the reader feels some part of the interest and amusement I always experience in watching the curious eighteenth century "poetic" mind at work, he may well feel that I have read more subtlety into my poets than they possessed. On at least one occasion I have forestalled critics by answering my own question as to whether I was considering too curiously. Yet the eighteenth century mind *was* allusive, analogical, tortuous; I suspect that the oversubtlety is theirs rather than mine. If literary students should be led by these pages to read or reread the *Opticks*, they will find rich reward. My own growing respect and affection for that work, so much less familiar to students of literature than is the *Principia*, has been best expressed by the Newton of our time, Albert Einstein:

"Fortunate Newton, happy childhood of science! He who has time and tranquillity can by reading this book live again the wonderful events which the great Newton experienced in his younger days. Nature was to him an open book, whose letters he could read without effort. The conceptions which he used to reduce the material of experience to order seemed to flow spontaneously from experience itself, from the beautiful experiments which he ranged in order like playthings and describes with an affectionate wealth of detail. In one person he combined the experimenter, the theorist, the mechanic, and, not least, the artist in exposition. He stands before us strong, certain, and alone: his joy in creation and his minute precision are evident in every word and in every figure."

Department of English   M.H.N.
Columbia University

CONTENTS

CHAPTER ONE

THE POPULAR RECEPTION OF THE OPTICKS

GREAT NEWTON'S DEAD, FULL-RIPE HIS FAME;
CEASE, VULGAR GRIEF, TO CLOUD OUR SONG:
WE THANK THE AUTHOR OF OUR FRAME,
WHO LENT HIM TO THE WORLD SO LONG.[1]

I

"THE immortal dinner came off in my painting-room," Benjamin Haydon wrote in his diary for December 28, 1817.[2] "Wordsworth was in fine cue, and we had a glorious set-to—on Homer, Shakespeare, Milton, and Virgil. Lamb got exceedingly merry and exquisitely witty, and his fun in the midst of Wordsworth's solemn intonations of oratory was like the sarcasm and wit of the fool in the intervals of Lear's passion. . . . He then in a strain of humour beyond description, abused me for putting Newton's head into my picture; 'a fellow,' said he, 'who believed nothing unless it was as clear as the three sides of a triangle.' And then he and Keats agreed that he had destroyed all the poetry of the rainbow by reducing it to its prismatic colours. It was impossible to resist him, and we all drank 'Newton's health, and confusion to mathematics.' "

Keats undoubtedly drank that toast with sincerity. Not long

[1] Allan Ramsay, "Ode to the Memory of Sir Isaac Newton: Inscribed to the Royal Society," in *Poems by Allan Ramsay*, London, 1731, II. 175.
[2] *The Autobiography and Memoirs of Benjamin Haydon. Edited from His Journals by Tom Taylor. A New Edition with an Introduction by Aldous Huxley*. London, 1926, I. 269.

[1]

after the "immortal dinner," he wrote the familiar lines in
Lamia:

> Do not all charms fly
> At the mere touch of cold philosophy?
> There was an awful rainbow once in heaven:
> We know her woof, her texture; she is given
> In the dull catalogue of common things.
> Philosophy will clip an Angel's wings,
> Conquer all mysteries by rule and line,
> Empty the haunted air, and gnomed mine—
> Unweave a rainbow.[3]

Wordsworth, in spite of his attitude toward such scientists as
would botanize upon their mothers' graves, may well have felt
an inward reservation as he drank. Lamb and Keats had not,
as he, spent formative years of their lives at Cambridge,

> where the statue stood
> Of Newton with his prism and silent face,
> The marble index of a mind for ever,
> Voyaging through strange seas of thought alone.[4]

Had Shelley attended Haydon's dinner, he might have refused to drink the toast. Certainly he would have argued stal-
wartly that Newton, far from destroying beauty with either
his *Principia* or his prism, had shown poets another kind of
"beauty" because he had shown them another kind of "truth."
Ironically enough, it was from the Newtonian prism that
Shelley chose his climactic figure of speech in his tribute to
the dead Keats. As Adonais became "a portion of the loveliness which once he made more lovely," he rose from darkness
through prismatic color to light:

> Life like a dome of many-coloured glass
> Stains the white radiance of Eternity,
> Until Death tramples it to fragments.[5]

[3] *Lamia,* II. 229-237.   [4] *Prelude,* III. 60-63.
[5] *Adonais,* ll. 462-464.

Shelley was intellectually close to the earlier eighteenth century poets to whom the Newtonian discoveries of light and color had come as a revelation. A greater poet than any of them, he experienced, as did they, surprise and excitement when he discovered new scientific theories.[6] Keats, to be sure, showed himself momentarily responsive to the emotions of a discoverer, whether "stout Cortez" or "some watcher of the skies, when a new planet swims into his ken." But Keats never understood another kind of scientific excitement, experienced by Halley, Newton, and Hooke and reflected by the eighteenth century poets, who watched for the return of a comet, realizing not only that the comet was governed by natural laws, but that man might deduce these laws and anticipate the comet's return "faithful to his time." To Shelley as to Thomson natural laws, whether of comets or of light and color, were both "just" and "beauteous." Keats might acknowledge the justice; he denied the beauty.

During the last few years critics have become increasingly aware of the impact of Newtonian theories upon literary imagination, and the extent to which poets read implications into something loosely called "Newtonianism."[7] For the most

[6] A study of Shelley's response to science may be found in Carl Grabo, *A Newton Among Poets*, Chapel Hill, 1930. While Mr. Grabo is particularly concerned with Shelley's attitude toward chemistry—suggested, as he says, by Alfred North Whitehead in *Science and the Modern World*—he has considered Shelley's response to the *Principia*; he occasionally mentions the *Opticks*, but has not, I think, seen the extent to which Shelley's figures of speech of light and color were influenced by his study of Newton.

[7] With no intention of offering a bibliography, I mention the early pioneer-study of Howard Mumford Jones, "Albrecht von Haller and English Philosophy," *P.M.L.A.*, XL (1925), 103-127; the various important articles of Herbert Drennon on Thomson's "Newtonianism," a list of which may be found in the recent book by Alan Dugald McKillop, *The Background of Thomson's Seasons*, Minneapolis, 1942, pp. 6-7. Mr. McKillop discusses Thomson's "Newtonianism," though he, like Mr. Drennon, is chiefly concerned with the *Principia*. There is a great deal of bibliographical material—particularly on poems which appeared at the time of Newton's death—in Hoxie Neale Fairchild, *Religious Trends in English Poetry, 1700-1740*, New York, 1939, *passim*.

part such critics have concerned themselves with the *Principia*. But the *Opticks* was even better known to laymen, since it was written in English, and dealt with processes of nature much more comprehensible and of more immediate concern, particularly to those poets to whom light and color have always been the stuff of poetry. The reader who turns from the descriptive poetry of the seventeenth century to that of the eighteenth is at least subconsciously aware that something new has occurred both in the interest of poets in light and color and in their technique in handling them. So far as the obsession with light is concerned, we have been inclined to attribute it to the influence of the poet who "blinded by excess of light" remained "dark, dark, dark beneath the blaze of noon." The Miltonic influence was very important; yet there was a different attitude complementing, and in the hands of lesser poets, distorting the Miltonic tradition. To understand the full radiance of the light which shines in so much eighteenth century poetry, we must add to the influence of Milton that of Newton. When we study color and light in detail, we shall find not only new observation, new technique, a groping for a new vocabulary, but also a growing interest in light and color in connection with the "Sublime" and "Beautiful" which came to a climax in Burke's *Enquiry*.

But the effect of the *Opticks* was not only in the realm of aesthetics. "Scientific" poets as these were, they labored to understand the physics of light, and still more the physics of sight, becoming acutely aware of the structure and function of the human eye, that mysterious liaison between the world "out there" and the mind "in here." Sight was exalted as the greatest of the senses; through their self-consciousness about one sense, the poets became more fully aware of the functions of all the senses, of their "harmony," interrelationship, interdependence. "Philosophical" poets, they grappled with the supposed "metaphysics" of the *Opticks*—as interpreted particularly by Locke—reading into Newton philosophical profundities which he himself would have regretted. In their response to the "science" of color and light in the *Opticks*, we shall find the poets of the first half-century unanimous in their agreement and their praise. They will agree well enough, too, in the "aesthetic" they developed. When we face the implications of the supposed "metaphysics," however, we shall see them parting company, and shall find significant differences between the three major poems of 1744, Young's *Night Thoughts*, Akenside's *The Pleasures of Imagination*, and Thomson's *Seasons,* each of which, in its way, was a "Newtonian" poem. Perhaps, too, we shall better understand the separation between "man" and "nature," against which the poets of high-Romanticism revolted. But these are matters for the future.

"Newton demands the Muse," Richard Glover wrote in his tribute to the memory of England's justest pride. That demand was to be paid, full measure, running over. The response of the poets to Newton is one of the many ironies of literary history, for Newton himself had little feeling for the Muse, showed no interest in aesthetics, and felt acute embarrassment at the fact that his age considered him a metaphysical thinker. He would have been puzzled and perplexed by the adulation of the poets in the period of his deification; perhaps the one poetic response which would have seemed to him justified was that of William Blake, who presided over his damnation.

II

"In a very dark Chamber, at a round Hole, about one third Part of an Inch broad, made in the Shut of a Window, I placed a Glass Prism, whereby the Beam of the Sun's Light, which came in at that Hole, might be refracted upwards toward the opposite Wall of the Chamber, and there form a colour'd Image of the Sun."[8] So Newton began his descrip-

[8] *Opticks: Or, a Treatise of the Reflections, Refractions, Inflections and*

tion of the simple experiment which led to theories of the relationship between light and color familiar to all of us today. We too have seen the spectrum Newton watched on his Cambridge walls, shading from the "least refrangible" red to the "most refrangible" violet through the primary and compound colors which Newton called "homogeneal" and "heterogeneal." "It's manifest" even to the least scientific among us, as Newton said,[9] that "the Sun's light is an heterogeneous Mixture of Rays, some of which are constantly more refrangible than others," and that upon such refrangibility depend the colors of natural bodies, since "some natural Bodies reflect some sorts of Rays, others other sorts more copiously than the rest. Minium reflects the least refrangible or red-making Rays most copiously. . . . Violets reflect the most refrangible most copiously, and thence have their Colour, and so of other Bodies. Every Body reflects the Rays of its own Colour more copiously than the rest, and from their excess and predominance in the reflected light has its Colour."[10] In Newton's hands, "the Science of Colours" became, as he said, "a Speculation as truly mathematical as any other part of Opticks."

More than a decade before the *Principia* appeared, Newton's hypotheses of the relationship between light and color were known to scientists, as the result of a paper which Newton sent to the Royal Society on February 6, 1672. His theories may have been known to Cambridge students as early as 1668-69, since, when Newton succeeded Barrow, his first lectures were upon optics. During his own university days he had observed and measured lunar crown and halos; he had bought a prism, through which he made his first discoveries of the relation between light and color. As yet, I have found

Colours of Light, reprinted from the fourth edition . . . by E. T. Whittaker, New York, 1931, Book I, Part I, Proposition II, p. 26. Page references in later notes are to this edition.

[9] *Ibid.*, Book I, Part I, Proposition II, p. 63.
[10] *Ibid.*, Book I, Part II, Proposition X, p. 179.

no evidence that those early lectures of Newton on optics affected lay imagination; nor, so far as I have seen, did the fellows at Cambridge realize how novel were the optical theories of their younger associate.[11] While Newton's theories, as outlined in his letter, were discussed with interest by members of the Royal Society, his hypotheses of the transmission of light were not generally accepted at first, the scientists still inclining rather to theories of Halley, Hooke, and Huygens. Hooke had opposed Newton's theories of color with such vehemence that for a time Newton was discouraged from further publication. In 1692, however, encouraged by the reception of the *Principia*, he decided to complete the *Opticks*, and had apparently done so when fire broke out in his rooms, destroying many papers, "among them a large work on Optics, containing the experiments and researches of twenty years." Not until 1704 did he finally publish the work; it was, perhaps, more than coincidence that he did not send it to press until after the death of Hooke in 1703.

Before this time, however, his prismatic discoveries were well known and influential. Locke had accepted them before he published the *Essay Concerning Human Understanding* in 1690, as comparison between the expanded work and the early draft of 1672 will make abundantly clear. One of Addi-

[11] It is curious that Henry More, for example, never mentions Newton's theories of optics, since he himself was much interested in the subject, and, long after he departed from his early allegiance to Cartesianism in general, continued to teach Descartes' *Dioptrics*. More was greatly interested in Newton, who like himself was a native of Grantham, and whose early education at the Grantham Grammar School had been under the direction of one of More's disciples, with the result that Newton was already under the spell of Cambridge Platonism when he entered the university, as his notebooks show. While More speaks of the fact that Newton "had a singular genius to mathematics" (*Conway Letters*, New Haven, 1930, p. 478), he was much more concerned with Newton's apocalyptical theories. I recall passing references to Newton's "mathematical genius" in letters and notes of Cambridge fellows which I read when I was working upon the *Conway Letters*, but I do not remember that any one of them mentioned his optical theories.

son's letters shows that the Newtonian theories were known in France in the last years of the seventeenth century when Addison was making his Grand Tour. He wrote to Dr. John Hough, Bishop of Lichfield, on November 29, 1700, about his earlier visit to "the Pere Melbranch"[12]: "His book is now Reprinting with Additions, among which he read to me a very pretty Hypothesis of Colours, which is very different from that of Cartesius or Dr. Newton, tho they may all three be true." Dr. John Arbuthnot, who followed scientific discoveries with keen interest, also writing in 1700, indicated a general acquaintance with new theories of light and color, and his awareness that Newton was working upon an expanded version of the paper which he had presented to the Royal Society.[13]

Yet although the theories were known before the publication of the *Opticks*, they did not at first make any particular

[12] *Letters of John Addison*, edited Walter Graham, Oxford, 1941, p. 25. Addison is referring to the *Récherche de la Vérité*, which had first appeared in 1674.

[13] He wrote in his "Essay on the Usefulness of Mathematical Learning," his note to which is signed "25 Novemb. 1700" (*Miscellaneous Works of the Late Dr. Arbuthnot*, Glasgow, 1751, I. 13-14):

"The next considerable object of Natural knowledge, I take to be Light. How unsuccessful enquiries are about this Glorious Body without the help of Geometry, may appear from the empty and frivolous discourses and disputations of a sort of Men, that call themselves Philosophers; whom nothing will serve perhaps, but the knowledge of the very Nature, and intimate Causes of every thing: while on the other hand, the Geometers not troubling themselves with those fruitless enquiries about the Nature of Light, have discovered two remarkable properties of it, in the reflexion and refraction of its beams; and from those, and their streightness in other cases, have invented the noble Arts of Opticks, Catoptricks and Dioptricks; teaching us to manage this subtile Body for the improvement of our knowledge, and useful purposes of Life. They have likewise demonstrated the cause of several Coelestial appearances, that arise from the inflection of its Beams, both in the Heavenly Bodies themselves and other Phaenomena, as *Parabolia*, the *Iris*, &c., and by a late Experiment they have discovered the celerity of its motion. And we shall know yet more surprizing properties of Light, when Mr. Newton shall be pleased to gratify the World with his *Book of Light and Colours*."

appeal to the poet or the layman. Even after 1704, when the first edition appeared, we do not find a widespread response of the lay imagination. However, even passing references to the new theories of color and light in the period between the first edition of the *Opticks* and the death of Newton are interesting enough to detain us briefly. While Addison did not devote a complete paper in *The Spectator* to Newton's optical theories, he mentioned them, phrased several references to color in Newtonian terms, and showed various effects of the new hypotheses. Blackmore indicated his knowledge of both the *Principia* and the *Opticks* in the *Creation*, which he published in 1712, though he was more interested in theories of transmission of light than in the prism.[14]

The young Pope suggested the interest of later poets in new figures of speech afforded by optical theories. In the "Essay on Criticism," he used the prism to describe false rhetoric:

> False Eloquence, like the prismatic glass,
> Its gaudy colours spreads on ev'ry place;
> The face of Nature we no more survey,
> All glares alike, without distinction gay:
> But true expression, like th' unchanging Sun,
> Clears and improves whate'er it shines upon;
> It gilds all objects, but it alters none.[15]

In the same poem he suggested the relationship of colors to light:

> When the ripe colours soften and unite,
> And sweetly melt into just shade and light.[16]

Pope's most charming early adaptation of prismatic color and light occurred in his descriptions of the sylphs and sylphids in

---

[14] Abstract as he always is, Blackmore seldom mentions color in the *Creation*; two passages on color which may conceivably reflect Newton's prism are so vague that I omit them. I shall return to Blackmore and Addison.

[15] "Essay on Criticism," ll. 311-317.   [16] Ibid., ll. 488-489.

passages which he added to the early version of *The Rape of the Lock*. As "secure the painted vessel glides, The sun-beams trembling on the floating tides," the Sylph, "with careful thoughts opprest," summons the lucid squadrons of "his Denizens of air." Among the "Fays, Fairies, Genii, Elves, and Daemons" are some who ordinarily live in the realms of ether, where their colors disappear in pure light:

> Some in the fields of purest Aether play, ·
> And bask and whiten in the blaze of day.[17]

But as they and others of the sylphs and sylphids descend to perform their terrestrial duties, light is refracted into color:

> Some to the sun their insect-wings unfold,
> Waft on the breeze, or sink in clouds of gold;
> Transparent forms, too fine for mortal sight,
> Their fluid bodies half dissolv'd in light,
> Loose to the wind their airy garments flew,
> Thin glitt'ring textures of the filmy dew,
> Dipt in the richest tincture of the skies,
> Where light disports in ever-mingling dyes,
> While every beam new transient colours flings,
> Colours that change whene'er they wave their wings.[18]

There are references to the prismatic discoveries in several of Pope's contemporaries in this early period, yet on the whole they indicate only that the discoveries of Newton's prism were familiar to the poet, though as yet he displayed only casual interest in finding new figures of speech. Among poets who wrote before the death of Newton, John Hughes alone suggested the kind of tribute we shall later find. His *Ecstasy*

---

[17] *The Rape of the Lock*, II. 77-78.
[18] *Ibid.*, II. 59-68. Pope used the same figure in *The Dunciad*, IV. 537-541:

> On others' Int'rest her gay liv'ry flings,
> Int'rest that waves on Party-colour'd wings:
> Turned to the Sun, she casts a thousand dyes,
> And, as she turns, the colours fall or rise.

was printed in 1720, when its author had been dead for three years; the exact date of composition remains surmise, yet before 1717 Hughes had written a little "cosmic voyage" in which he anticipated a host of later poets whose tributes to Newton after his death were also celestial voyages. Newton was still alive when Hughes, whose soul was to precede Newton's in its journey to the empyrean, wrote:

> The great Columbus of the skies I know!
> 'Tis Newton's soul, that daily travels here
> In search of knowledge for Mankind below.
> O stay, thou happy Spirit, stay,
> And lead me on thro' all the unbeaten Wilds of Day.[19]

In part Hughes followed the model which Edmund Halley had offered to poets, when he versified the discoveries of the *Principia* in his Latin poem prefixed to the first edition; but Hughes was a pioneer in combining in verse the theories of the *Opticks* with those of the *Principia*, as he did in later lines:

> Here let me, thy Companion, stray,
> From Orb to Orb, and now behold
> Unnumber'd Suns, all Seas of molten Gold;
> And trace each Comet's wand'ring Way,
> And now descry Light's Fountain-Head,
> And measure its descending Speed;
> Or learn how Sun-born Colours rise
> In Rays distinct, and in the Skies,
> Blended in yellow Radiance flow,
> Or stain the fleecy Cloud, or streak the Wat'ry Bow;
> Or now diffus'd their beauteous Tinctures shed
> On ev'ry Planet's rising Hills, and ev'ry verdant Mead.

III

WIDESPREAD interest of poets in the *Opticks* began in 1727, at the time of Newton's death, when the feeling for "Britain's justest pride" amounted almost to deification. In this

---

[19] *The Ecstasy*, London, 1735, II. 307; also in Chalmers, X. 60-62.

period the *Opticks* came into its own, sometimes second to the *Principia*, sometimes even more interesting. Practically all the eulogies and elegies written in 1727 and 1728 mentioned at least "Newton's rainbow" and "Newton's colours"; but with a single exception the poems of 1727 were still crude and amorphous, so far as the *Opticks* was concerned. The lesser poets were waiting for a "pattern" which would assist them in versifying the technicalities of the optical theories, as Halley's poem had aided them with the Newtonian planets, moon, and comets. Such a poetic model for the future was provided by James Thomson in his poem "To the Memory of Newton,"[20] written at the time of Newton's death and published during the same year. Thomson's debt to Halley's poem is obvious; he followed him in the general discussion of universal gravitation; he too concerned himself with "our wandering Queen of Night," and with the effect of the moon on tides and with comets. While Thomson may have known Hughes' *Ecstasy*, his versification of the discoveries of the *Opticks* went beyond Hughes:

> Even Light itself, which every thing displays,
> Shone undiscovered, till his brighter mind
> Untwisted all the shining robe of day;
> And, from the whitening undistinguished blaze,
> Collecting every ray into his kind,
> To the charmed eye educed the gorgeous train
> Of parent colours.[21]

From this time forth, the characteristic tribute to the *Opticks* began with an invocation or apostrophe to light; then the poets, again following Thomson, called the roll of the "par-

[20] "To the Memory of Sir Isaac Newton," in *The Complete Poetical Works of James Thomson*, edited J. L. Robertson, London and New York, 1908, pp. 436-442. All references to Thomson, unless otherwise indicated, are to this variorum edition.
[21] *Ibid.*, ll. 96-102.

ent colours," usually mentioned the rainbow,[22] and concluded, as did Thomson, with a suggestion that Newton had shown the poet new beauty in the natural world:

> Did ever poet image aught so fair,
> Dreaming in whispering groves by the hoarse brook?
> Or prophet, to whose rapture heaven descends?[23]

Richard Glover's eulogy,[24] published the following year, possibly modeled upon Thomson's, also assisted succeeding poets, for while Glover's poem was less charming than Thomson's, it was more technical, and so appealed to the semi-scientific versifiers. To Glover, Newton's achievement in the *Opticks* was not second to that in *Principia*. Having paid tribute to the theory of universal gravitation, he turned to the discovery of the nature of light:

> Nor here the sage
> Big with invention still renewing staid.
> But O bright angel of the lamp of day,
> How shall the muse display his greatest toil?
> Let her plunge deep in Aganippe's waves,
> Or in Castalia's ever-flowing stream,
> That re-inspired she may sing to thee,
> How Newton dar'd advent'rous to unbraid
> The yellow tresses of thy shining hair.
> Or didst thou gracious leave thy radiant sphere,
> And to his hand thy lucid splendours give,

[22] Thomson's roll call of the colors and his rainbow-passage are discussed below.

[23] "To the Memory of Newton," ll. 119-121.

[24] Glover's "A Poem on Newton" appeared in Henry Pemberton, *A View of Sir Isaac Newton's Philosophy*, London, 1728; it may be found more conveniently in Chalmers, XVII. 13-16. I have followed the text in the Pemberton edition, in spite of the fact that since it is unpaginated, I cannot give specific references; the text in Chalmers varies slightly from that in the original: for example, in the passages quoted, Glover spoke of the *Opticks* as Newton's "*greatest* toil," while Chalmers reads "*greater* toil."

> T'unweave the light-diffusing wreath, and part
> The blended glories of thy golden plumes?[25]

From light, Glover went on to Newtonian color:

> He with laborious, and unerring care,
> How diff'rent and imbodied colours form
> Thy piercing light, with just distinction found.
> He with quick sight pursu'd thy darting rays,
> When penetrating to th' obscure recess
> Of solid matter, there perspicuous saw,
> How in the texture of each body lay
> The power that separates the diff'rent beams.
> Hence over nature's unadorned face
> Thy bright diversifying rays dilate
> Their various hues. . . .[26]

In his suggestion that the discoveries of the *Opticks* were equal in importance to those of the *Principia*, Glover was following Henry Pemberton, with whose *View of Sir Isaac Newton's Philosophy* his eulogy was published. Newton himself had written to Oldenburg that he considered his early discoveries about light and color as "the oddest, if not the most considerable detections which hath hitherto been made in the operations of Nature." Pemberton went further:

> . . . to turn our eyes to that other philosophical work, his treatise of Optics, in which we shall find our great author's inimitable genius discovering it self no less, than in the former; nay perhaps even more. . . . Nor yet is this work inferior to the other in usefulness; for as that has made known to us one great principle in nature, by which the celestial motions are continued, and by which the frame of each globe is preserved; so does this point out to us another principle no less universal, upon which depend all those operations in the smallest parts of matter, for whose sake the greater frame of the universe is erected.[27]

[25] "A Poem on Newton."   [26] Ibid.
[27] *A View of Sir Isaac Newton's Philosophy*, London, 1728, Book III, Chapter 1, pp. 316-317.

Voltaire, who was spending exile-years in England at the time of Newton's death, took much the same position in his *Lettres Anglaises*, when he said that "the Philosophers of the last Age found out a new Universe; and a circumstance which made its Discovery more difficult, was, that no one had as much as suspected its Existence." Having spoken of Galileo, Kepler, Harvey, and Boyle, he turned to Newton, and after considering his hypothesis of gravitation, continued: "The several discoveries which Sir Isaac Newton has made on Light are equal to the boldest Things which the Curiosity of Man could expect, after so many philosophical Novelties."[28] Voltaire, like many of his English contemporaries, wrote a poem of Newtonian tribute,[29] in which he too followed the general pattern which Halley established, and though he later insisted[30] that the Newtonian philosophy, founded as it was on geometry, was no fit subject for poetry, he somewhat weakened the force of his argument by still another versification of Newtonian principles.

Voltaire's belief that Newton's "geometry" was not a fitting subject for poetry was shared by the better English Newtonian poets, though the poetasters sometimes attempted to versify Newton's mathematics; but that there were nonmathematical implications in the *Opticks* which could and did form new themes for poetry, we shall see. The poets were assisted not only by the models of Thomson and Glover, but by such popular expositions as that offered by Pemberton in a work particularly designed for the layman, who, as Pemberton's prospectus suggested, might better grasp "the Force and Beauty of this great Genius . . . when the simple and genuine Productions of the Philosopher are disengaged from the

28 *Letters Concerning the English Nation*, London, 1926, Letter XVI, pp. 107 ff.
29 "A Madame La Marquise du Chatelet" (1738), in *Œuvres Complets de Voltaire*, Paris, 1785, Tome 13.
30 In his reply to the "Anti-Lucretius" of Cardinal de Polignac.

Problems of the Geometrician."[31] "Science for the layman" had long been popular. Fontenelle's *Conversations on a Plurality of Worlds* was still eagerly read in both French and English; such encyclopedias as those contained in the "Boyle Lectures" found a wide audience. Pemberton, quite aware that the "Gentleman" felt it his duty, as well as pleasure, to be *au courant* with all important scientific developments, yet that he like Milton's Eve appreciated "grateful digressions," addressed his book to the intelligent layman:

> Every Gentleman, who has a moderate Degree of Literature or Politeness, may by this Assistance form a comprehensive View of the stupendous Frame of Nature, and the Structure of the Universe, with the same Ease he now acquires a Taste of the Magnificence of a Plan of Architecture, or the Elegance of a beautiful Plantation; without engaging in the minute and tedious Calculations necessary to their Production.

Other scientific writers, such as Desaguliers, MacLaurin, Martin, and Ferguson, followed Pemberton in expositions of Newtonian theories; William Derham in the many editions of his *Physico-Theology* and *Astro-Theology* discussed the *Principia* and the *Opticks*; such scientific popularizers as L'Abbé Pluche made the Newtonian theories still simpler.

The "Ladies" were not far behind the "Gentlemen" in their enthusiasm. Henry Jones, in "Philosophy, a Poem, addressed to the ladies who attended Mr. Booth's Lectures in Dublin,"[32] reminded them of the lectures on Newtonian color and light:

> Behold, ye Fair! how radiant Colours glow,
> What dyes the Rose; what paints the heav'nly Bow,
> The purpling Shade, the rich refracted Ray,
> And all th' unblended Beams of various Day.

[31] *London Journal*, April 16, 1726; quoted McKillop, *Background of Thomson's Seasons*, p. 12.

[32] Henry Jones, *Poems on Several Occasions*, London, 1749, pp. 22-26.

[16]

While most of the Newtonian popularizations were equally concerned with the *Principia* and the *Opticks*, one of the most widely read was devoted entirely to the *Opticks*. Francesco Algarotti's *Il Newtonianismo per le Dame*,[33] first published in 1737, was familiar to English readers not only in the beautiful Italian editions, but in at least two English translations. It was fitting that as a woman—Aphra Behn—had translated Fontenelle's *Conversations on a Plurality of Worlds* for her countrywomen, so Elizabeth Carter translated Fontenelle's Italian successor. Here the ladies found the *Opticks* interpreted specifically for them by a "Philosopher," who knew English literature well, and who was able to lead his "Lady" by easy stages from an admiration of Pope's poetry to an understanding of Newton's physics.

With such poems as Thomson's and Glover's for models, and with an ever-increasing number of expositions and popularizations of Newton ready to their hands, eighteenth century poets found it easy to understand and versify the discoveries suggested in the *Opticks*. Casual allusions to the theories of color and light are frequent in the poetry of the second quarter-century. Like the earlier telescope and microscope, the prism afforded new figures of speech. Thomson, discussing the Greek philosophers, wrote in *Liberty*:

[33] *Il Newtonianismo per le Dame, ovvero Dialoghi sopra la luce e i colore*, Napoli, 1737. Another beautifully bound and illustrated edition appeared in 1739; an *"editione sesta"* is listed as of 1746, and still another in 1752. The English translation by Elizabeth Carter appeared as *Sir Isaac Newton's Philosophy Explain'd for the Use of Ladies*, London, 1739. The British Museum Catalogue lists a second edition, London, 1742, and another edition, Glasgow, 1765. The only copy of the supposed second edition I have been able to see is that in the New York Public Library, of which the title page is defaced; it is attributed in the catalogue to Elizabeth Carter. My impression is that this is an entirely different work by another translator; it bears the title *Sir Isaac Newton's Theory of Light and Colours and his Principle of Attraction*. The style is quite different, and, as the title indicates, this edition also contains a popular exposition of the *Principia*.

O'er all shone out the great Athenian sage,
And father of philosophy—the sun,
From whose white blaze emerged each various sect
Took various tints, but with diminished beam.[34]

Pope in his later work used figures of light and color frequently, sometimes for satiric purposes, as in a couplet in *The Dunciad*:

Did Nature's pencil ever blend such rays,
Such varied light, in one promiscuous blaze?[35]

He wrote more seriously in his *Moral Essays*:

Court-virtues bear, like Gems, the highest rate,
Born where Heaven's influence scarce can penetrate:
In life's low vale, the soil the Virtues like,
They please as beauties, here as wonders strike.
Though the same Sun with all-diffusive rays
Blush in the Rose, and in the Diamond blaze.[36]

Various poets used the theories of light and color for tribute and compliment, as did Savage in elegiac lines:

And now the Muse heaven's milky path surveys,
With thee, 'twixt pendent worlds, it wondering strays,
Worlds which, unnumber'd as thy virtues, roll
Round suns—fix'd, radiant emblems of thy soul!
Hence lights refracted run through distant skies,
Changeful on azure plains in quivering dyes!
So thy mind darted through its earthy frame,
A wide, a various, and a glittering flame.[37]

Casual allusions and random figures of speech—there are many of them in the period—are of only passing interest. More important are the attempts on the part of versifiers to answer the supposed "demand" for the Muse, and express Newtonian theories in verse; and much more important is the

---

[34] *Liberty*, II. 222-225.   [35] *Dunciad*, IV. 411-412.
[36] *Moral Essays, Epistle I*. 141-146.
[37] Richard Savage, "To the Countess of Rochford," in Johnson, *Works*, Vol. 45, pp. 143-144.

fact that, through their study of Newton, poets came to look upon nature with new eyes, and to develop a descriptive poetry different from that of earlier generations in its careful and often technical use and description of color and light. Let us first, therefore, observe light refracted through the eighteenth century prism, and see what the poets found in the colors that emerged.

CHAPTER TWO

COLOR AND LIGHT IN THE DESCRIPTIVE POETS

MYRIADS OF MINGLING DYES FROM THESE RESULT,
AND MYRIADS STILL REMAIN—INFINITE SOURCE
OF BEAUTY, EVER FLUSHING, EVER NEW.
DID EVER POET IMAGE AUGHT SO FAIR,
DREAMING IN WHISPERING GROVES BY THE HOARSE BROOK?
OR PROPHET, TO WHOSE RAPTURE HEAVEN DESCENDS?[1]

I

THE profound symbolism which Milton felt in light is too familiar to be rehearsed at length. In part because of his philosophic and poetic heritage, in part because of his blindness, Light remained to him remote, godlike, awful. It was both the essence of divinity and the garment of Deity—"dark with excessive light Thy skirts appear." The "Author of all Being" was the

Fountain of Light, thyself invisible
Amidst the glorious brightness where thou sitt'st
Thron'd inaccessible.[2]

No single passage from *Paradise Lost* was more familiar to the eighteenth century poets than the invocation in Book III:

Hail, holy Light, offspring of Heaven first-born!
Or of th' Eternal coeternal beam
May I express thee unblamed? since God is light,
And never but in unapproached light,
Dwelt from eternity, dwelt then in thee,

[1] Thomson, "To the Memory of Sir Isaac Newton," ll. 116-121.
[2] *Paradise Lost*, III. 374-376.

> Bright effluence of bright essence increate!
> Or hear'st thou rather pure ethereal stream,
> Whose fountain who shall tell? before the Sun,
> Before the Heavens, thou wert, and at the voice
> Of God, as with a mantle didst invest
> The rising world of waters dark and deep,
> Won from the void and formless infinite!

Echoes of that invocation, with phrases from other prologues and from Satan's address to the Sun, recur constantly among the later poets. Yet the differences are as striking as the similarities. Thomson, Savage, Mallett, did not forget Milton but they also remembered Newton. They reminded their readers that the ultimate source of light is God, but they were even more aware that the immediate source of light is the sun, a physical body which, in spite of its pre-eminence in the solar system, is nevertheless responsive to laws of nature which man had come to comprehend. Thomson's apostrophe to light in "Summer" shows both similarities and differences, but for the moment we may compare with Milton's invocation one of Christopher Smart's[3] in which the fusion of Miltonic and Newtonian elements may be clearly seen. Smart too began with God and light:

> The thought-kindling light,
> Thy prime production, darts upon my mind
> Its vivifying beams, my heart illumines,
> And fills my soul with gratitude and thee.

But as the poet continued, light was refracted into color:

> Hail to the cheerful rays of ruddy morn,
> That paints the streaky east . . .
> Hail to the freshness of the early breeze,
> And Iris dancing on the new-fall'n dew!
> Without the aid of yonder golden globe
> Lost were the garnet's lustre, lost the lily,

[3] Christopher Smart, "On the Goodness of the Supreme Being"; Chalmers, XVI. 35.

The tulip and auricula's spotted pride;
Lost were the peacock's plumage, to the sight
So pleasing in its pomp and glossy glow.
O thrice-illustrious! were it not for thee
Those pansies, that reclining from the bank,
View through th' immaculate, pellucid stream
Their portraiture in the inverted Heaven,
Might as well change their triple boast, the white,
The purple, and the gold, that far outvie
The eastern monarch's garb, ev'n with the dock,
Ev'n with the baneful hemlock's irksome green.

"Fairest of beings! first created light!" became, even more than it had been to Milton, the "prime cause of beauty":

for from thee alone
The sparkling gem, the vegetable race,
The nobler worlds that live and breathe, their charms,
The lovely hues peculiar to each tribe,
From thy unfailing source of splendour draw![4]

Newton might say that, thanks to his prism, the "Science of Colours" had become a truly mathematical speculation, but the interest of the descriptive poets in the *Opticks* had nothing to do with mathematics. It is no exaggeration to say that Newton gave color back to poetry from which it had almost fled during the period of Cartesianism. Like Galileo before him and Locke after him, Descartes had regarded the primary qualities of size, shape, figure as the only inherent properties of natural objects or of the ultimate atoms. Until Newton's experiments the geometrical conception of nature had not been extended to color. Although, as we shall later see, the "Newtonian philosophy" came to be involved with the Cartesian and the Lockean, there is no question that the first effect of Newton's resolution of the colors and his careful analyses of their properties was to produce a new scientific

[4] David Mallett, *The Excursion*; Chalmers, XIV. 22.

grasp of a richer world of objective phenomena peculiarly sympathetic to poets.

To the descriptive poets of the Age of Newton, light was the source of beauty because it was the source of color. This is a persistent refrain in the period. While light was glorious in itself, it was most immediately and obviously beautiful when it was refracted into color, affording beauty, as Glover said, to Nature's otherwise "unadorned face":

> whatever charms,
> Whatever beauties bloom on Nature's face,
> Proceed from thy all-influencing light.[5]

The pattern once established, it was followed so persistently by poets that an address to the sun was almost invariably followed by at least a passing reference to its effect on color. From the "rich-stained rays" of the "Parent of Seasons . . . reflected various, various colours rise."[6] "The Sun his welcome light . . . casts through the air, renewing Heaven's face With heaven-born beauty."[7] "What gay creative power his presence brings," wrote Savage in a description of sunrise:

> the face of things,
> All night beneath successive shadows miss'd,
> Instant begins in colours to exist.[8]

There was hardly a descriptive poet of the period who did not either in theory or practice reiterate the idea that

> Thy Colours paint the Sky's ethereal Blue,
> And stain the lifted Rainbow's varying Hue,
> Diversify the Clouds with Tinctures gay,
> And thro' thy Depths is shed the golden Day.[9]

[5] "A Poem on Sir Isaac Newton," *ed. cit.*
[6] James Thomson, "Summer," first edition, 1727; *ed. cit.*, p. 121.
[7] David Mallett, *The Excursion*; Chalmers, XIV. 19.
[8] Richard Savage, *The Wanderer*, in Johnson, *Works*, Vol. 45, p. 50.
[9] Moses Browne, "Essay on the Universe," in *Poems on Several Subjects*, London, 1739, p. 315.

Samuel Boyse varied the conventional pattern slightly by returning his colors back to the light from which they came:

> . . . mingling gems the borrow'd day unfold,
> And the rich purple waves emboss'd with gold;
> Yet mark this scene of painted grandeur yield
> To the fair lily that adorns the field!
> Obscur'd, behold that fainter lily lies,
> By the rich bird's inimitable dyes;
> Yet these survey confounded and outdone
> By the superior lustre of the Sun;
> That Sun himself withdraws his lessen'd beam
> From thee, the glorious Author of his frame.[10]

In this period when the "philosophic eye" was trained to
see color in terms of light, we are likely to happen upon passing references to the new theory in unexpected places. One
would hardly look for "Newtonianism" in such a poem as
Somerville's *Chase*, yet the finale is a paean of praise to the
great discoverer; and in early morning when "from the ken-
nel rush the joyous pack," the poet momentarily sees the
hounds in prismatic hues:

> The rising Sun, that o'er th' horizon peeps,
> As many colours from their glossy skins
> Beaming reflects, as paint the various bow
> When April showers descend.[11]

Thomson's "reptile young," called forth by the light of summer, are also reminiscent:

> by myriads forth at once
> Swarming they pour, of all the varied hues
> Their beauty-beaming parent can disclose.[12]

Many poets described insects in prismatic terms, watching—
as had Pope earlier—the succession of colors and light on
wings; Henry Brooke went into detail in a long passage in

[10] Samuel Boyse, "Deity"; Chalmers, XIV. 552.
[11] William Somerville, *The Chase*, II. 104-107; Chalmers, XI. 159.
[12] "Summer," ll. 247-249.

which he described both larvae and the emergent winged creatures:

> Each spangled back bright sprinkling specks adorn,
> Each plume imbibes the rosy tinctur'd morn;
> Spread on each wing the florid seasons glow,
> Shaded and verg'd with the celestial bow,
> Where colours blend an ever varying dye,
> And wanton in their gay exchanges vie.[13]

Savage's Wanderer, that far-traveller who liked what'er he looked on, and whose looks went everywhere, could find beauty in light reflected even by the sea-calf!

> Spread on yon rock the sea-calf I survey:
> Basked in the sun, his skin reflects the day.[14]

With Newtonian eyes, the poets discovered new beauties in the most familiar aspects of nature, which had always been the stuff of poetry: in individual colors seen through the prism, in the rainbow, in sunrise and sunset, in the succession of colors throughout the day. There entered into eighteenth century descriptive poetry what might be called a "symbolism of the spectrum," which came to its height in Thomson, yet which was suggested by various poets. Sometimes the prismatic colors were described by and for themselves:

> Some range the colours as they parted fly,
> Clear-pointed to the philosophic eye;
> The flaming red, that pains the dwelling gaze,
> The stainless, lightsome yellow's gilding rays;
> The clouded orange, that betwixt them glows,
> And to kind mixture tawny lustre owes;
> All-chearing green, that gives the spring its dye;
> The bright transparent blue, that robes the sky;
> And indico, which shaded light displays,
> And violet, which in the view decays.

[13] Henry Brooke, *Universal Beauty*, V. 276-281; Chalmers, XVII. 361.
[14] Richard Savage, *The Wanderer*; Johnson, *Works*, Vol. 45, p. 50.

> Parental hues, whence others all proceed;
> An ever-mingling, changeful, countless breed,
> Unravel'd, variegated, lines of light,
> When blended, dazzling in promiscuous white.[15]

Thomson, whom Savage was here following, had done the same sort of thing with more poetic charm in his verses to Newton. Immediately following the description of the "whitening undistinguished blaze" of light, he introduced the "gorgeous train Of parent colours":

> First the flaming red
> Sprung vivid forth; the tawny orange next;
> And next delicious yellow; by whose side
> Fell the kind beams of all-refreshing green.
> Then the pure blue, that swells autumnal skies,
> Ethereal played; and then, of sadder hue,
> Emerged the deepened indigo, as when
> The heavy-skirted evening droops with frost;
> While the last gleamings of refracted light
> Died in the fainting violet away.[16]

Other poets called the roll of colors in connection with gems:

> Through sparkling gems the plastic artists play,
> And petrify the light's embody'd ray;
> Now kindle the carbuncle's ruddy flame,
> Now gild the chrysolite's transparent beam;
> Infuse the sapphire's subterraneous sky,
> And tinge the topaz with a saffron dye;
> With virgin blush within the ruby glow,
> And o'er the jasper paint the show'ry bow.[17]

The seventeenth century poets had also loved gems, particularly those which were their heritage from the Bible; perhaps they loved them even more than did their descendants of the eighteenth century, who became too self-conscious—like

[15] *Ibid.*, p. 67.
[16] "To the Memory of Newton," ll. 102-111.
[17] Henry Brooke, *Universal Beauty*, III. 47-54; Chalmers, XVII. 346.

Mammon, "the least erected Spirit that fell," always more concerned with estimating the value of the "riches of Heaven's pavement, trodden gold" than with the "vision beatific." Carew had written of

> The constant diamond, the wise chrysolite,
> The devout sapphire, em'rald apt to write
> Records of memory, cheerful agate, grave
> And serious onyx, topaz that doth save
> The braines calm temper, witty amethyst,
> This precious quarry, or what else the list
> On Aaron's ephod . . .[18]

Carew's stones came to him from Exodus; their symbolism was as old as the language of flowers, drawn from astrology, physiology, legend, and superstition. William Thompson in the eighteenth century drew his heavenly gems from the Apocalypse, but combined Scripture with Newtonian science; the laws of refraction held in heaven as on earth:

> A mirror spreads its many-colour'd round,
> Mosaic-work, inlaid by hands divine
> In glist'ring rows, illuminating each,
> Each shading: beryl, topaz, chalcedon,
> Em'rald and amethyst. Whatever hues
> The light reflects, celestial quarries yield,
> Or melt into the vernant-showry bow,
> Profusive, vary here in mingling beams.[19]

No poet combined the Newtonian science with gems so deftly and charmingly as did James Thomson. In "Summer," the light which streams from the central sun affects every part of nature, animate and inanimate. Diving beneath the "surface of the enlivened earth," into the "embowelled cavern . . . darting deep" it wakens the precious stones:

[18] Thomas Carew, "Epitaph on the Lady S.," in *Poems*, edited Arthur Vincent, London, n.d., p. 78.
[19] William Thompson, "Sickness"; Chalmers, XV. 50.

The unfruitful rock itself, impregned by thee,
In dark retirement forms the lucid stone.
The lively diamond drinks thy purest rays,
Collected light compact. . . .
At thee the ruby lights its deepening glow,
And with a waving radiance inward flames.
From thee the sapphire, solid ether, takes
Its hue cerulean; and, of evening tinct,
The purple-streaming amethyst is thine.
With thy own smile the yellow topaz burns;
Nor deeper verdure dyes the robe of Spring,
When first she gives it to the southern gale,
Than the green emerald shows. But, all combined,
Thick through the whitening opal play thy beams;
Or, flying from its surface, form
A trembling variance of revolving hues
As the site varies in the gazer's hand.[20]

Here are the red, yellow, green, blue, violet of the spectrum,
but here is also something much more subtle and charming—
the resolution of light into colors, and the return of colors
back to light. Thomson begins with the white light of the
diamond, watches in the spectrum the ruby's red, the yellow

[20] "Summer," ll. 140-159. These lines, particularly those on the opal,
are reminiscent of Newton's experiment with his comb-shaped instrument,
which he reports in *Opticks*, Book I, Part II, Proposition V; *ed. cit.*, pp.
140-141: "But if I so much accelerated the Motion, that the Colours by
reason of their quick Succession could not be distinguished from one another, the Appearance of the single Colours ceased. There was no red, no
yellow, no green, no blue, nor purple to be seen any longer, but from a
Confusion of them all there arose one uniform white Colour. . . . If the
Impressions follow one another slowly, so that they may be severally perceived, there is made a distinct Sensation of all the Colours one after
another in a continual Succession. But if the Impressions follow one another so quickly, that they cannot be severally perceived, there ariseth out
of them all one common Sensation, which is neither of this Colour alone
nor of that alone, but hath it self indifferently to 'em all, and this is a
Sensation of Whiteness. By the Quickness of the Successions, the Impressions of the several Colours are confounded in the Sensorium, and out of
that Confusion ariseth a mix'd Sensation."

[28]

of the topaz, the green of the emerald, the "hue cerulean" of
the sapphire, and the purple of the amethyst, with its evening
tint. All the colors come together in the "whitening opal,"
which dimly reflects each of them, and which begins to return
them to the white light from which they were derived.

Sometimes the poets, instead of merely calling the catalogue of the colors, showed themselves pondering various
associations of Newton's prismatic discoveries. Savage's
Wanderer, standing on a cliff by the sea, found his mind
turning, like Newton's, to telescopic lenses:

> There lies obscur'd the ripening diamond's ray,
> And thence red-branching coral's rent away.
> In conic form there gelid crystal grows;
> Through such the palace-lamp, gay lustre throws!
> Lustre, which, through dim night, as various plays
> As play from yonder snows the changeful rays!
> For nobler use the crystal's worth may rise,
> If tubes perspective hem the spotless prize;
> Through these the beams of the far-lengthen'd eye
> Measure known stars, and new remoter spy.[21]

Later on his travels the Wanderer discovered in the Hermit's
cave an adaptation of the Newtonian discoveries. In his
chapel the Hermit proudly showed his guest his "storied
windows richly dight":

> Here the transfigur'd Son from earth retires;
> See! the white form in a bright cloud aspires!
> Full on his followers bursts a flood of rays,
> Prostrate they fall beneath th' overwhelming blaze!
> Like noon-tide summer-suns the rays appear,
> Unsufferable, magnificent, and near![22]

As the Wanderer continued on his journey, his philosophic
eye watched for the new beauties in nature. It was he who

[21] Richard Savage, *The Wanderer*, in *Works*, edited Johnson, Vol. 45,
p. 12. The lines are followed by a tribute to Halley.
[22] *Ibid.*, pp. 22-23.

felt at sunrise that "the face of things All night beneath successive shadows miss'd, Instant *begins in colours to exist.*"
He watched colors in the rainbow, in flowers, and insects :

> Now from the full-grown day a beamy shower
> Gleams on the lake, and gilds each glossy flower.
> Gay insects sparkle in the genial blaze,
> Various as light, and countless as its rays; . . .
> Now, from yon range of rocks, strong rays rebound,
> Doubling the day on flowery plains around :
> King-cups beneath far-striking colours glance,
> Bright as th' etherial glows the green expanse,
> Gems of the field !—the topaz charms the sight,
> Like these, effulging yellow streams of light.[23]

Most obviously, of course, the prism was associated by poets with "Newton's rainbow," for in spite of Newton's own careful statement about his predecessors,[24] the rainbow was and remained Newton's. To the eighteenth century poets, as to Keats, Newton alone had explained and unwoven it. Both Glover and Thomson introduced the rainbow into their tributes to Newton immediately after describing the prismatic colors. Glover wrote :

> and hence when vernal rains
> Descending swift have burst the low'ring clouds,
> Thy splendors through the dissipating mists

---

[23] *Ibid.*, p. 55.

[24] *Opticks*, Book I, Part II, Proposition IX, Problem iv; *ed. cit.*, p. 169: "It is now agreed upon, that this Bow is made by Refraction of the Sun's Light in Drops of falling Rain. This was understood by some of the Antients, and of late more fully discover'd and explain'd by the famous Antonius de Dominis, Archbishop of Spalato, in his Book *De Radiis Visus & Lucis*, published by his Friend Bartolus at Venice, in the Year 1611, and written above 20 Years before. For he teaches there how the interior Bow is made in round Drops of Rain by two Refractions of the Sun's Light, and one Reflexion between them, and the Exterior by two Refractions, and two sorts of Reflexions between them in each Drop of Water. . . . The same Explication Des-Cartes hath pursued in his Meteors, and mended that of the exterior Bow." Newton adds, however, that these earlier writers had not understood the true origin of color.

[30]

In its fair vesture of unnumber'd hues
Array the show'ry bow.[25]

Thomson, too, had turned from the spectrum to the rainbow:

These, when the clouds distil the rosy shower,
Shine out distinct adown the watery bow;
While o'er our heads the dewy vision bends
Delightful, melting on the fields beneath.
Myriads of mingling dyes from these result,
And myriads still remain—infinite source
Of beauty, ever flushing, ever new.[26]

The poem on Newton was written in 1727; in the following
year Thomson described the Newtonian rainbow in "Spring":

Meantime, refracted from yon eastern cloud,
Bestriding earth, the grand ethereal bow
Shoots up immense; and every hue unfolds,
In fair proportion running from the red
To where the violet fades into the sky.
Here, awful Newton, the dissolving clouds
Form, fronting on the sun, thy showery prism;
And to the sage-instructed eye unfold
The various twine of light, by thee disclosed
From the white mingling blaze.[27]

In his description of the rainbow, as in his comet-passage in
"Summer," Thomson contrasted the attitude of the "fond
sequacious herd" who feared the comet and the swain who
"runs to catch the falling glory" of the rainbow with that of
the "enlightened few Whose godlike minds philosophy ex-

[25] "A Poem on Newton."
[26] "To the Memory of Sir Isaac Newton," ll. 112-118.
[27] "Spring," ll. 203-212. I am purposely quoting the lines as they appeared in the later revised editions (*Poetical Works*, p. 10). As Mr. McKillop has said (*Background of Thomson's Seasons*, p. 59), the lines on the rainbow "proved intractable; Thomson rewrote them in the post-1738 edition, and again in 1744, evidently troubled by the need for scientific exactness in his epithets." All the Newtonian ideas, however, were present in the first version. Thomson has another more conventional rainbow-passage in *Liberty*, Part V, ll. 549 ff.

alts." The difference between Thomson and Keats is not entirely one of period, for Shelley would have agreed with Thomson. One adjective, used by both Thomson and Keats, is significant. Keats said in *Lamia*: "There was an *awful rainbow* once in heaven." Thomson used the same adjective with different connotation: "Here, *awful Newton* . . ." We are not yet ready to consider one implication which might be read into those passages—that the "awe" felt by the eighteenth century poets was less for a miracle of God than for the thinking mind of man which had come to comprehend laws of nature, whether in the rainbow or the "law of love" of the planets. To Keats glory and loveliness passed away when scientists attempted to strip Nature and leave her exposed and bare. In his mind the eighteenth century poets had "taken on the mysteries of things as if they were God's spies"; they, like Newton, had destroyed the poetry of the rainbow by reducing it to its prismatic form. Yet there is one glory of the moon, another of the sun—and the eighteenth century poets adored the greater luminary, symbol of Light, symbol of Reason, the "Newtonian Sun." The sun was never more beautiful to them than when it shone in full meridian splendor, its light streaming through ether in straight lines, refracted as little as possible by atmosphere, cloud, or mist. They delighted in their own intellectual maturity, feeling that they had outgrown the childlike attitude of the simple swain who seeks a pot of gold, or of Noah, to whom the rainbow was miracle. They did not believe that Newton had taken beauty from poetry; he had added new beauty, because he had added new truth. Akenside felt the beauty of the new truth as strongly as Thomson:

> Speak, ye, the pure delight, whose favour'd steps
> The lamp of science thro' the jealous maze
> Of nature guides, when haply you reveal
> Her secret honours: whether in the sky,

The beauteous laws of light, the central pow'rs
That wheel the pensile planets round the year. . . .[28]

The rainbow afforded him the best possible illustration of
modern man's response to the "beauteous laws of light":

Nor ever yet
The melting rainbow's vernal-tinctur'd hues
To me have shone so pleasing, as when first
The hand of science pointed out the path
In which the sun-beams gleaming from the west
Fall on the watry cloud, whose darksome veil
Involves the orient; and that trickling show'r
Piercing, thro' every crystalline convex
Of clust'ring dew-drops to their flight oppos'd,
Recoil at length where concave all behind
Th' internal surface of each glassy orb
Repells their forward passage into air;
That thence direct they seek the radiant goal
From which their course began; and, as they strike
In diff'rent lines the gazer's obvious eye,
Assume a diff'rent lustre, thro' the brede
Of colours changing from the splendid rose
To the pale violet's dejected hue.[29]

As in gems and in the rainbow, so in the succession of
colors at various times of day, from earliest dawn to late twilight, the eighteenth century poets observed the spectrum.
Glover was groping toward the technique which Thomson
was best to employ when he wrote:

At thy approach
The morning risen from her pearly couch
With rosy blushes decks her virgin cheek;
The ev'ning on the frontispiece of heav'n

[28] *Pleasures of Imagination*, London, 1744, II. 126-131.
[29] *Ibid.*, ll. 103-120. I am limiting myself to these few examples, since the
theme is so obvious. While many versifiers described the rainbow, they
added nothing, and, when they entered into extended description, were
usually following Thomson and Glover.

> Her mantle spreads with many colours gay;
> The mid-day skies, in radiant azure clad,
> The shining clouds, and silver vapours rob'd
> In white transparent intermix'd with gold,
> With bright variety of splendor cloath
> All the illuminated face above.[30]

Mallet handled the prismatic colors of the day more deftly in the first book of *The Excursion*.[31] At dawn we notice only light: "A whitening lustre shoots its tender beam"; as the sun rises, "sun-tinctur'd, changeful hues" begin to show. We are first aware of red:

> The western grey of yonder breaking clouds
> Slow-reddens into flame . . .
>   the flush'd horizon flames intense
> With vivid red, in rich profusion stream'd
> O'er Heaven's pure arch. . . .

As light increases, all the spectrum-colors appear, when the sun invests

> Her ample bosom, earth, air, sea, and sky,
> In one bright robe, with heavenly tinctures gay.

After the clouds and mists disappear, we see the pure azure of ether:

>   the aerial concave without cloud,
> Translucent, and in purest azure drest.

At high noon "the fervent Sun, Full-blazing o'er the blue immense, burns out with fierce effulgence," and we are conscious less of color than of light. But in late afternoon and early evening, as clouds gather and mist rises, we observe the last weaker colors of the spectrum, as in morning we saw the first:

>   Yon evening clouds,
> Lucid or dusk, with flamy purple edg'd,
> Float in gay pomp the blue horizon round.

[30] "Poem on Newton," *ed. cit.*; Chalmers, XVII. 14.
[31] *The Excursion*; Chalmers, XIV. 17-21.

On the whole the interest of the "Newtonian" poets in color and light was in the larger rather than in the smaller aspects of nature. Occasionally one finds passing reminiscences of Newton's observations on bubbles[32] and "Of the permanent Colours of natural Bodies." Others than Christopher Smart, in the passage already quoted, watched "Iris dancing on the new-fall'n dew," and some noticed, as had Newton, that "the Webs of some Spiders, by being spun very fine, have appeared color'd." Newton's observation of the colors in peacocks' tails was repeated, as was his comment that "the finely colour'd Feathers of some Birds . . . appear of several Colours in several Positions of the Eye."[33] The flower descriptions of the eighteenth century, however, still remain conventional and generalized; the poets do not yet number the streaks on the tulip, though occasionally we detect a new approach in such a description as this of the passionflower:

> All-beauteous flow'r, whose centre glows
> With studs of gold: thence streaming flows,
> Ray-like effulgence. Next is seen
> A rich expanse of varying hue,
> Enfring'd with an empurpled-blue,
> And streak'd with young Pomona's green.[34]

But as a group they were more interested in detecting color-similarities in the macrocosm and microcosm, such as William Thompson suggested:

> Have ye not seen, in gentle even-tide,
> When Jupiter the Earth hath richly shower'd,
> Striding the clouds, a bow dispredden wide
> As if with light inwove, and gaily flower'd
> With bright variety of blending dies?

[32] The bubbles are discussed in *Opticks*, Book II, Part I, and *passim*.

[33] These observations may be found in *Ibid.*, Book II, Part III, Proposition V; *ed. cit.*, pp. 251 ff.

[34] Walter Harte, "The Enchanted Region"; Chalmers, XVI. 380.

White, purple, yellow melt along the skies,
Alternate colours sink, alternate colours rise.

The Earth's embroidery then have ye ey'd,
And smile of blossoms, yellow, purple, white;
Their vernal-tinctur'd leaves, luxurious, dy'd
In Flora's livery, painted by the light.
Light's painted children in the breezes play,
Lay out their dewy bosoms to the ray,
Their soft enamel spread, and beautify the day.[35]

In their more careful and precise observation of color and
their attempts to describe it accurately, the poets of this generation seem to us like amateurs who sincerely "love color"
or "love music," after their eyes and ears have been trained
to a truer understanding of the painter's use of color, the
musician's mathematics of harmony. Their former "love" is
not destroyed; it is rather enhanced by a new appreciation.
The eighteenth century poets lifted up their eyes to the skies;
they saw the rainbow and observed the refraction of light
through cloud and mist; they enjoyed even more than in the
past the clarity of unrefracted light in ether, and the clear
colors of a brilliant day:

What boundless tides of splendour o'er the skies,
O'erflowing brightness, stream their golden rays!
Heaven's azure kindles with the varying dies,
Reflects the glory, and returns the blaze.
Air whitens; wide the tracts of ether been,
With colours damask'd rich, and goodly sheen,
And all above is blue; and all below is green.[36]

But, like our Newtonian ancestors, having observed the refraction of light into the colors of the spectrum, let us return
them to the light from which they were derived, and consider the eighteenth century obsession—the word is used ad-
visedly—with Light itself.

[35] William Thompson, "An Hymn to May"; Chalmers, XV. 34.
[36] Ibid.

II

Nature and Nature's laws lay hid in night;
God said, "Let Newton be!" and all was light.[37]

So FAR as the eighteenth century poets were concerned, Pope
did not exaggerate. Light is everywhere in the poetry of the
second quarter-century, in figures of speech, in day-poems
imitated from "L'Allegro," even in the night-pieces of poets
who self-consciously turned away from a light so powerful
that it became unbearable. Milton's influence is still clear,
though, like the moon, he shone by reflected light after "Newton rose, in orient beauty bright." The light which shines so
persistently in poetry of this period is, of course, not entirely
either Milton's or Newton's. Much of it goes back to remote
ancestors whom they shared in common—Hebraic, Christian,
Pythagorean, Neo-Platonic. The first miracle of God was the
creation of light in nature, the miracle of the last day the
creation of the light of man's reason, the *lumen animae*, as
St. Augustine called it. To the Pythagoreans and the Neo-
Platonists light was a mystical symbol; so, too, it was to St.
John. God is light; the Logos, the Son, is also light. "That
was the true Light which lighteth every man that cometh into
the world." The symbolism of light was persistent in the
period of the Renaissance, which delighted in the fusion of
Hebraic, Christian, Platonic elements. Light is everywhere
in Bacon: in his figures of torches and branched candlesticks,
in his diamond sparkling in pure light, his pearl showing best
in varied light, his "dry light" of reason, his "Merchants of
Light." It was a favorite figure of the seventeenth century
philosophers, whether the Cartesian *lumière naturelle* or the
Galilean *lumen naturale*. Newton's own recognized religious
and mystical tendencies made it easy for the poets to read
into his austere intellectual theories emotional responses
which, indeed, he shared with such mystic-scientists as Kep-

[37] Alexander Pope, "Epitaph Intended for Sir Isaac Newton."

ler. Tributes to the great discoverer were almost universally
couched in figures of the light whose nature he discovered.
Cosmic voyagers took off on wings of their imagination to
find his departed soul among the radiant spheres:

> The god-like man now mounts the sky,
> Exploring all yon radiant spheres;
> And in one view can more descry
> Than here below in eighty years.[38]

They visualized "Britain's justest pride" arriving before the
throne of Deity, cherubim and seraphim paying to him hom-
age which, in Dante and Milton, had been reserved for the
"Fountain of Light":

> Even now the sons of light,
> In strains high warbled to seraphic lyre,
> Hail his arrival in the coast of bliss.[39]

His name, they sang, would be remembered as long as light
remained; it would sink into oblivion only when the last
great darkness covered the globe:

> when the Suns he lighted up, shall fade,
> And all the worlds he found, are still decay'd;
> Then void, and waste, Eternity shall lie,
> And Time, and Newton's name, together die.[40]

The poets vied with each other to find epithets and adjectives with which to describe both "uncreated light" and the
light of the sun. Even though we detect earlier phrases, there
is much in their lines which came to the poets from Newton:

> Illustrious name, irrefragable proof
> Of man's vast genius and the soaring soul!

[38] Allan Ramsay, "Ode to the Memory of Sir Isaac Newton," *ed. cit.*,
II. 175.
[39] James Thomson, "To the Memory of Sir Isaac Newton," ll. 5-7.
[40] Aaron Hill, "Epitaph on Sir Isaac Newton," in *Works* (second edition), London, 1744, III. 44-45.

From him they turned to the Source of Light, as did Smart in this particular passage:

> Yet what were thou to him, who knew his works
> Before creation form'd them. . . .
> Who shone supreme, who was himself the light
> Ere yet Refraction learn'd her skill to paint,
> And bend athwart the clouds her beauteous bow.[41]

Old figures of speech came back in this generation with new significance. Light was "the spark, the light, the lamp, the ray, Essence or effluence of Essential Day"[42]; it was a "bright emanation of the Godhead," a "fountain of living lustre."[43] The sun was the "fountain of light and colour, warmth of life! The king of glory!"[44] It was the "fountain of the golden day,"[45] the "radiant ruler of the year," the "ocean of flame"[46]:

> this great spring of uncreated might!
> This all-resplendent orb of vital light;
> Whence all-created beings take their rise,
> Which beautify the Earth, or paint the skies.[47]

The Deity of the eighteenth century—different though He was in so many ways—dwelt amidst

> the blaze of uncreated light . . .
> Whose pure effulgence, radiant to excess,
> No colours can describe, or words express.[48]

His creation, "delightful Nature," was a "child of heavenly light"[49]; his creation, man, was "a beam ethereal, sullied, and absorpt," "a beam, a mere effluvium of his majesty."[50] Even

---

[41] Christopher Smart, "On the Omniscience of the Supreme Being"; Chalmers, XVI. 32.
[42] Henry Brooke, *Universal Beauty*; Chalmers, XVII. 351.
[43] Walter Harte, "Essay on Reason"; Chalmers, XVI. 354.
[44] David Mallett, *The Excursion*; Chalmers, XIV. 17.
[45] Mark Akenside, "For the Winter Solstice"; Chalmers, XIV. 97.
[46] David Mallett, *op. cit.*, p. 23.
[47] Samuel Boyse, "Deity"; Chalmers, XIV. 545.
[48] Ibid., p. 552.
[49] Samuel Boyse, "Triumph of Nature"; Chalmers, XIV. 534.
[50] Edward Young, *Night Thoughts*, I. 76; IV. 419-420.

"Science" which was mysteriously both his creature and the chief evidence for his existence was a "fair diffusive ray from the great source of mental day," which with "resistless light" dispersed phantoms and shades of night.[51] Adjective was hurled upon epithet, Pelion piled upon Ossa, until the modern reader murmurs ungratefully, "Mine eyes dazzle!"

Even after the "cosmic voyage" of the seventeenth century settled into the "excursion" of the eighteenth century,[52] with its interest in this world rather than in the heavens, the "excursion" poets—and there were many—devoted long sections of their poems to apostrophes and invocations to light, in which Newton was constantly celebrated. David Mallett in *The Excursion* divided his attention equally between the earth and the heavens, devoting one book of his poem to each; so too did Moses Browne in his "Essay on the Universe." In such poems we find a distinction which will later become important: color was associated with the terrestrial world and with beauty; light radiated in the books or passages devoted to the heavens, and was associated less with beauty than with sublimity.

As we have already seen in connection with the growing interest in color, light took on new interest to the descriptive poets, resulting in closer and more accurate descriptions than poetry had hitherto known of the appearance of light at different times of day, of shade and shadow, of the luminary bodies. The poets sought a more technical and exact vocabulary in which to describe phenomena long seen and appreciated by poets. Milton had been content with a general description of light and shade in "L'Allegro" and "Il Penseroso," which were the literary sources of so many day- and night-poems of the eighteenth century. He paused only momentarily over sunrise:

[51] Mark Akenside, "Hymn to Science"; Chalmers, XIV. 132.
[52] I am discussing in detail this change from the "cosmic" poetry of the seventeenth century to the "excursion" poetry of the eighteenth in a forthcoming book.

Right against the eastern gate,
Where the great Sun begins his state,
Robed in flames and amber light,
The clouds in thousand liveries dight.

The eighteenth century poets were not content with such generalized descriptions. Since we have already seen the new interest of the period in color at various times of day in one of Mallett's poems, we may well turn to another of his day-poems[53] in order to see how the Newtonian descriptive poets handled light. As Aurora appears "all-unveiled,"

The vast horizon on Amyntor's eye
Pours full its scenes of wonder, wildly great,
Magnificently various . . . and all beheld
More lovely in the Sun's adorning beam,
Who now, fair-rising o'er yon eastern cliff,
The vernal verdure tinctures gay with gold.

Aurelius addresses the sun:

Source of life and love!
Whose smile now wakes o'er Earth's rekindling face
The boundless blush of spring.

Morning passes; midday comes:

the mounted Sun
Full, from the midmost, shot in dazzling stream
His noon-tide ray.

In the afternoon,

The lamp of day, though from mid-noon declin'd,
Still flaming with full ardor, shot on Earth,
Oppressive brightness round; till in soft steam
From Ocean's bosom his light vapour's drawn,
With grateful intervention o'er the sky
Their veil diffusive spread.

And, as evening comes,

He, glorious from amidst
A pomp of golden clouds, th' Atlantic flood

[53] David Mallett, "Amyntor and Theodora"; Chalmers, XIV. 29-34.

> Beheld oblique, and o'er its azure breast
> Wav'd one unbounded blush.

There is hardly a descriptive poet of the period who does not show an interest in the laws of light. They liked to contrast light seen through "atmosphere" with light in "pure unclouded aether":

> As darts the Sun oblique his varied rays,
> When through the fleecy cloud his lustre plays,
> Here deepens to a gloom the varied green,
> There beams a light—and shifts the shadowy scene:
> But when the obvious vapour melts away,
> The boundless prospect brightens into day.[54]

They described the "noon-day's stainless beam," "th'aerial concave without cloud, Translucent, and in purest azure drest,"[55] pausing for moments like this:

> As o'er the blue expanse with golden light,
> The orient Sun ascending spreads his ray.[56]

Dyer upon Grongar Hill described his landscape as it appeared in light as "pure" as is ever possible in our terrestrial globe:

> Now I gain the mountain's brow,
> What a landscape lies below!
> No clouds, no vapours intervene,
> But the gay, the open scene
> Does the face of Nature show,
> In all the hues of Heaven's bow!
> And, swelling to embrace the light,
> Spreads around beneath the sight.[57]

No poet of the mid-century, however, responded to Newtonian color and light more fully than did Thomson in *The Seasons*, and no other poet so well used the new techniques.

[54] Samuel Boyse, "Triumphs of Nature"; Chalmers, XIV. 536.
[55] David Mallett, *The Excursion*; Chalmers, XIV. 17.
[56] Samuel Boyse, "Ode on the Birth of the Marquis of Tavistock"; Chalmers, XIV. 525.
[57] John Dyer, "Grongar Hill"; Chalmers, XIII. 223.

III

STANDING upon Greenwich Hill, as he pondered Newton's discovery of the nature of color and light, James Thomson watched a sunset—as he had watched a rainbow—with Newtonian eyes:

> Even now the setting sun and shifting clouds,
> Seen, Greenwich, from thy lovely heights, declare
> How just, how beauteous the refractive law.[58]

The "justice" and the "beauty" of Newtonian law is a recurrent motif in Thomson's poetry. As philosophical and as scientific as the professed "philosophical" and "scientific" poets we shall later consider, Thomson was nevertheless primarily a poet, with a poet's need for and response to beauty. He admired the surpassing intellectual attainments of "Newton . . . our philosophic sun,"[59] "Newton, pure intelligence, whom God To mortals lent to trace his boundless works"[60]; he recognized the fact that Newton's scientific genius consisted in his formulation of "laws divinely simple"[61]:

> O unprofuse magnificence divine!
> O wisdom truly perfect! thus to call
> From a few causes such a scheme of things
> Effects so various, beautiful, and great.[62]

But as poet, he never ceased to stress the fact that, while the "effects" were various and great, they were also poetically beautiful.

In *The Seasons*, because of the very subject he set himself, Thomson was almost equally concerned with color and light. While he used all the colors of the spectrum, some were more significant than others. Indigo appears only once or twice; orange is almost conspicuous by its absence, as indeed it is in English landscape, though we might expect to find it more

[58] "To the Memory of Sir Isaac Newton," ll. 122-124.
[59] Ibid.   [60] "Summer," ll. 1560-1561.
[61] Ibid., l. 1562.   [62] "To the Memory of Newton," ll. 68-71.

often than we do in his exotic tropical scenes. Red is often
used, usually associated with morning; "violet, darkly blue,"
with few exceptions, is an evening color. Green, of course, is
persistent in the poem, as it is in nature; it was a color in
which Thomson found special pleasure. While red and violet
might be either beautiful or ominous, green—with a single
exception[63]—was a happy color. "Moist, bright, and green,
the landscape laughs around"[64]; in the Golden Age of the
World, spring "greened all the year."[65] "Gay green" was the
chief color of the "vivid verdure" and the "various hues" of
"vernant earth"[66]:

> chiefly thee, gay green!
> Thou smiling Nature's universal robe!
> United light and shade! where the sight dwells
> With growing strength and ever-new delight.[67]

More important, from the point of view of the *Opticks*, is
Thomson's treatment of azure and yellow. Rarely did Thomson use "azure" and "blue" interchangeably. "Azure" was
associated correctly with the sky, and, like Newton, Thomson
used it to describe the clarity of ethereal light in which there
is a minimum of refraction by moisture:

> The lessening cloud,
> The kindling azure, and the mountain's brow,

---

[63] "Autumn," ll. 952-954:

> a crowded umbrage, dusk and dun,
> Of every hue from wan declining green
> To sooty dark.

[64] "Spring," l. 198.
[65] Ibid., l. 320.
[66] Ibid., ll. 79 ff.
[67] Ibid., ll. 83-86. Mr. McKillop (*Background of Thomson's Seasons*,
pp. 57-58) has discussed this passage in connection with Addison's comment upon the artist's response to the "right mixture of light and shade" in
green. It needed no ghost of Newton come from the nether world to make
either a landscape-artist or a landscape-poet conscious of the special significance of green; yet the position of the color in the spectrum may have
had something to do with Thomson's persistent emphasis upon it.

Illumined with fluid gold, his near approach
Betoken glad.[68]

After a summer storm:

As from the face of Heaven the shattered clouds
Tumultuous rove, the interminable sky
Sublimer swells, and o'er the world expands
A purer azure.[69]

In "Autumn," as the "fierce effulgence" of summer departs
and mists begin to rise, azure imperceptibly changes to "a
serener blue," which "with golden light enlivened wide invests the happy world."[70]

Of all colors, the "golden light" of yellow was most beautiful to Thomson; it occurs most frequently in *The Seasons*,
and seems to have possessed a kind of mystical significance.
In "Spring" we see the "woods with yellow lustre bright,"[71]
and

a yellow mist,
Far smoking o'er the interminable plain,
In twinkling myriads lights the dewy gems.[72]

In "Summer" the "valleys float with golden waves"[73]; the
mountain brow is "illumined with fluid gold"; later, "Autumn's yellow lustre gilds the world."[74] In the rainbow, the
"glittering robe of joy" is "set off abundant by the yellow
ray."[75] Newton, too, in the *Opticks*, had frequently paused
over yellow, calling attention to the facts that so-called "white
light," is usually "yellow light," that homogeneal yellow,
with its heterogeneal companion orange, is "the most luminous of the Prismatick Colours . . . in the Focus of those
Rays which are in the middle of the orange and yellow; there
where the Colour is most luminous and fulgent. . . ."[76] In

[68] "Summer," ll. 82-85.   [69] "Summer," ll. 1223-1226.
[70] "Autumn," ll. 25-27.   [71] "Spring," l. 737.
[72] Ibid., ll. 194-196.   [73] "Summer," l. 1448.
[74] "Autumn," l. 1322.   [75] "Summer," ll. 1229-1230.
[76] *Opticks*, Book I, Part I, Proposition VII.

yellow Thomson felt the radiance of light: "With thine own smile the yellow topaz burns." On the one hand, yellow as a color was beautiful; on the other, in its effulgence it approached sublimity. But we are not yet ready to distinguish between the "Sublime" and the "Beautiful" in light and color.

More than any of the other poets, Thomson developed what has been called the "symbolism of the spectrum." We have already seen him following the colors through the spectrum: "flaming red," "tawny orange," "delicious yellow," "all-refreshing green," "pure blue," "and then, of sadder hue . . . the deepened indigo," associated with the "heavy-skirted evening" and with frost as "the last gleamings of refracted light Died in the fainting violet away." We have seen, too, that he played delightedly with the spectrum in his lines on gems and on the rainbow, in which the same general symbolism was implied. In his gem-passage, Thomson went still further, indicating not only the emergence of colors from pure light in the diamond, but their return to white light in the opal. Is it to consider too curiously to find the same symbolism in *The Seasons* as a whole?[77] As spring emerges from the icy arms of winter, we are conscious that

> Whate'er the Wintry frost
> Nitrous prepared, the various-blossomed Spring
> Put in white promise forth.[78]

Spring "lifts the white clouds sublime, and spreads them thin, Fleecy, and white."[79] "Fair-handed Spring . . . throws out the snowdrop and the crocus first"; the "hawthorn whitens"; only as spring progresses do "the varied colours run." Throughout the rest of "Spring," and throughout *The Seasons* as a whole, we almost forget white in nature until in "Winter" the year dies away, as it began, in the whiteness of

---

[77] Undoubtedly it is; yet I myself have had so much amusement in watching the eighteenth century mind at work that I suggest this at least as a possibility.

[78] "Autumn," ll. 4-6.   [79] "Spring," ll. 30-31.

snow, glittering frost, and ice. But we need not overlabor this particular analogy, which, while it actually exists in nature in northern climes, may not have occurred to James Thomson. Certainly the "symbolism of the spectrum" appears often in Thomson's sequence of colors in an individual day from the reds of dawn through the spectrum to the "sad violet" of evening, when color vanishes into darkness in which all colors are temporarily lost. Thomson was too good an artist to labor his symbolism obviously, but in at least one "Season," he followed the device of breaking white light into color, and returning his colors again to white light. Morning in "Summer" begins:

> The meek-eyed morn appears, mother of dews,
> At first faint-gleaming in the dappled east;
> Till far o'er ether spreads the widening glow,
> And, from before the lustre of her face,
> White break the clouds away.[80]

After running the gamut of colors and the succession of lights, day ends; "low walks the sun . . . gives one bright glance, then total disappears":

> sober Evening takes
> Her wonted station in the middle air,
> A thousand shadows at her beck. First this
> She sends on earth; then that of deeper dye
> Steals soft behind; and then a deeper still,
> In circle following circle, gathers round
> To close the face of things.[81]

As in the morning we were first conscious of white, so for a moment before total darkness blots out nature, we momentarily see whiteness again:

> Wide o'er the thistly lawn, as swells the breeze,
> A whitening shower of vegetable down
> Amusive floats.[82]

[80] "Summer," ll. 47-51.   [81] Ibid., ll. 1648-1654.
[82] Ibid., ll. 1658-1660. J. L. Robertson, in his variant edition of *The*

Thomson was a poet of color, but he was still more a poet of light. Like his master Milton, whose influence is clear throughout his poetry, he was even more susceptible to light than to color and read into it deeper symbolic meaning. His apostrophe to Light in "Summer," if taken from its context, seems only a paraphrase of Milton's invocations:

> Prime cheerer, Light!
> Of all material beings first and best!
> Efflux divine. Nature's resplendent robe,
> Without whose vesting beauty all were wrapt
> In unessential gloom; and thou, O Sun!
> Soul of surrounding worlds! in whom best seen
> Shines out thy Maker! may I sing of thee? . . .
> How shall I then attempt to sing of Him
> Who, Light Himself, in uncreated light
> Invested deep, dwells awfully retired
> From mortal eye or angel's purer ken;
> Whose single smile has, from the first of time,
> Filled overflowing all those lamps of heaven
> That beam forever through the boundless sky.[83]

Yet as Thomson followed the progress of light throughout a day or watched it at night, he showed an exactness of expression and an accuracy of observation which marks him as a Newtonian poet. Sometimes the exactness lies in his careful employment of terms which, formerly vague in poets, had now become technical. A good example may be found in his use of the word "ether." Newton himself, as we shall see, had said: "I do not know what this Aether is,"[84] yet his long

Seasons (_ed. cit._, p. 130), calls attention to the fact that this passage is a condensation of a longer one appearing in the editions of 1727 and 1728, that it was dropped in 1730, and restored in 1744. He feels that Thomson erred in the restoration, since, after a passage on the coming of night, he introduced what should have been invisible—whiteness. I am inclined to believe that Thomson reintroduced the passage deliberately for the reason I have suggested.

[83] "Summer," ll. 90-96; 175-181.

[84] See below, p. 65. Originally "ether" was a term which might be

discussions of ether and its function in connection with the
transmission of light made the intelligent layman self-conscious in the use of the word, particularly in discriminating
between "ether" and "atmosphere" or "air." Milton's At-
tendant Spirit in *Comus* had descended from "regions mild
of calm and serene *air*"; Satan upon his interplanetary journey "winds with ease Through the pure marble *air* his oblique
way"; as he stood upon the sun, "the *air*, Nowhere so clear,
sharpened his visual ray."[85] To Thomson, Summer, "child of
the Sun," came "from brightening fields of *ether* fair-dis-
closed"[86]; his distinction between "ether" and "air" or "atmosphere" may be seen in many careful descriptions of the
effect of clouds, mists, or fogs upon light. As a storm gathers
in spring:

> the effusive South
> Warms the wide air, and o'er the void of heaven
> Breathes the big clouds with vernal showers distent.
> At first a dusky wreath they seem to rise,
> Scarce staining ether; but by fast degrees,
> In heaps on heaps the doubling vapour sails
> Along the loaded sky, and mingling deep
> Sits on the horizon round a settled gloom.[87]

In "Winter":

> Hung o'er the farthest verge of heaven, the sun
> Scarce spreads o'er ether the dejected day.
> Faint are his gleams, and ineffectual shoot
> His struggling rays in horizontal lines

used either generally or specifically; it might mean the sky, or heaven;
Thomson uses the general sense of "ethereal" in "Winter," ll. 738-739:
"The full ethereal round," and in the first line of "Spring": "Come, gentle
Spring, ethereal mildness, come." To Aristotle, specifically, "ether" was a
fifth element, the celestial, forming the material of the heavenly spheres
and bodies. The "luminiferous ether," in the sense used by Thomson, is a
modern conception.

[85] *Paradise Lost*, III. 563-564; 619-620.
[86] "Summer," ll. 1-2.
[87] "Spring," ll. 144-151.

Through the thick air; as clothed in cloudy storm,
Weak, wan, and broad, he skirts the southern sky.[88]

Even more exact is a description in "Autumn":

Meantime, light shadowing all, a sober calm
Fleeces unbounded ether; whose least wave
Stands tremulous, uncertain where to turn
The gentle current; while, illumined wide,
The dewy-skirted clouds imbibe the sun,
And through their lucid veil his softened force
Shed o'er the peaceful world.[89]

Elsewhere in *The Seasons* a difference which we feel between Milton and Thomson in their treatment of light is the result of the fact that Thomson took for granted not only that light travels at incredible speed, but that it is everywhere diffused in the luminiferous ether. Satan, on his journey from world to world, believed that there were limits to light, as he found in the "dark illimitable ocean, without bound, Without dimension," that "hoary Deep" stretching beyond Hell, and in the "dark world" of Limbo, where he wandered long in gloom "till at last a gleam Of dawning light turned thitherward in haste His travelled steps." And for all Milton's interest in the Galilean astronomy, reflected in passing references in these very scenes, Satan on his visit to the sun harked back to such fictional hardy mariners as those of Lucian, who seemed as comfortable in the blazing sun as in the Hesperian isles. Nowhere did Satan indicate any discomfort as he stood in the full splendor of the "magnetic beam, that gently warms The universe"; yet this is the same Satan who so short a time before had used his tall spear "to support uneasy steps Over the burning marle," for "such resting found The sole of unblest feet"! Satan was child enough of the

[88] "Winter," ll. 44-49.
[89] "Autumn," ll. 957-963. Notice also in "Winter," ll. 692-697, the distinction between "the blue serene, For sight too fine," where "the ethereal nitre flies," and the "atmosphere": "Close crowds the shining atmosphere."

seventeenth century to show a keen intellectual interest in the
light of the sun, which he could now observe empirically:

> The place he found beyond expression bright,
> Compared with aught on Earth, metal or stone—
> Not all parts like, but all alike informed
> With radiant light, as glowing iron with fire. . . .
> Here matter new to gaze the Devil met
> Undazzled.[90]

But, in the eighteenth century, when the "soaring soul" of
Newton sailed among the spheres and flew "through those
endless worlds He here so well descried," he traveled among
the "radiant tracts on high" with the speed of light itself,
through a universe in which light was never-ceasing, until, at
journey's end, he was greeted by the "sons of light":

> Thy swift career is with the whirling orbs,
> Comparing things with things, in rapture lost,
> And grateful adoration for that light
> So plenteous rayed into thy mind below
> From Light Himself.[91]

"Summer" is, of course, the book of *The Seasons* in which
Thomson's descriptions of light and of the sun are most frequent, and in which reminiscences of the Newtonian theories
most abound.

> Yonder comes the powerful king of day. . . .
> Aslant the dew-bright earth and coloured air,
> He looks in boundless majesty abroad,
> And sheds the shining day, that burnished plays. . . .[92]

To the sun's light and heat all nature responds, but as day
goes on, heat and light become excessive:

> 'Tis raging noon; and vertical, the sun
> Darts on the head direct his forceful rays.
> O'er heaven and earth, far as the ranging eye
> Can sweep, a dazzling deluge reigns; and all
> From pole to pole is undistinguished blaze.[93]

---

[90] *Paradise Lost*, III. 591-614.
[91] Thomson, "To the Memory of Sir Isaac Newton," ll. 194-198.
[92] "Summer," ll. 81-88.   [93] Ibid., ll. 432-436.

Yet the light and heat of a northern climate are as nothing in comparison with the power of the sun in the torrid zone: "Climes unrelenting! with whose rage compared, Yon blaze is feeble and yon skies are cool," where

> the bright effulgent sun,
> Rising direct, swift chases from the sky
> The short-lived twilight, and with ardent blaze
> Looks gaily fierce o'er all the dazzling air.[94]

In temperate zones, even on the hottest day of midsummer, late afternoon and evening bring relief from the excess of light and heat:

> The Sun has lost his rage; his downward orb
> Shoots nothing now but animating warmth
> And vital lustre; that with various ray,
> Lights up the clouds, those beauteous robes of heaven,
> Incessant rolled into romantic shapes,
> The dream of waking fancy. . . .
> Low walks the sun, and broadens by degrees,
> Just o'er the verge of day. The shifting clouds,
> Assembled gay, a richly-gorgeous train,
> In all their pomp attend his setting throne.
> Air, earth, and ocean smile immense. And now
> As if his weary chariot sought the bowers
> Of Amphitrite and her tending nymphs,
> (So Grecian fable sung) he dips his orb;
> Now half-immersed; and now, a golden curve,
> Gives one bright glance, then total disappears.[95]

---

[94] Ibid., ll. 635-638.

[95] Ibid., ll. 1371-1376; 1620-1629. In the early edition of 1727 the last part of this passage showed its ancestry in the *Opticks* more clearly:

> Low walks the Sun, and broadens by degrees,
> Just o'er the Verge of Day. The rising Clouds,
> That shift, perpetual, in his vivid Train,
> Their dewy Mirrors, numberless, oppos'd,
> Unfold the hidden Riches of his Ray,
> And chase a Change of Colours round the Sky.

Thomson's observations of light gleaming through darkness are only less frequent than his descriptions of light during the day. Meteors, the "lambent lightning," a comet, the
moon and the stars, even the glow-worm, are described with
eighteenth century accuracy:

> When from the pallid sky the Sun descends,
> With many a spot, that o'er his glaring orb
> Uncertain wanders, stained; red fiery streaks
> Begin to flush around. The reeling clouds
> Stagger with dizzy poise, as doubting yet
> Which master to obey; while, rising slow,
> Blank in the leaden-coloured east, the moon
> Wears a wan circle round her blunted horns.
> Seen through the turbid fluctuating air,
> The stars obtuse emit a shivering ray;
> Or frequent seem to shoot athwart the gloom,
> And long behind them trail the whitening blaze.[96]

Thomson's moon in "Autumn" was his heritage from a long
line of scientific ancestors, beginning with Galileo, culminat-
ing in Newton; yet "oft, as if her head she bowed, stooping
through a fleecy cloud," she is reminiscent too of Milton:

>   Meanwhile the moon,
> Full-orbed and breaking through the scattered clouds,
> Shows her broad visage in the crimsoned east.
> Turned to the sun direct, her spotted disk
> (Where mountains rise, umbrageous dales descend,
> And caverns deep, as optic tube descries)
> A smaller earth, gives all his blaze again,
> Void of its flame, and sheds a softer day.
> Now through the passing cloud she seems to stoop,
> Now up the pale cerulean rides sublime.
> Wide the pale deluge floats, and streaming mild
> O'er the skied mountain to the shadowy vale,
> While rocks and floods reflect the quivering gleam,

[96] "Winter," ll. 118-129.

The whole air whitens with a boundless tide
Of silver radiance, trembling round the world.[97]

Thomson, however, was not only a "Newtonian" descriptive poet. Like his contemporaries, he was upon occasion both a "scientific" and a "philosophic" poet. He pondered both the physics of light and the physics of sight; he was aware of aesthetic and metaphysical implications which he and others read into the *Opticks*. For the moment we shall leave him, but we shall find ourselves returning to him again and again, since he included in himself all the interests of the day which we find among his contemporaries.

[97] "Autumn," ll. 1088-1102.

CHAPTER THREE

THE PHYSICS OF LIGHT IN THE SCIENTIFIC POETS

GIVE ME TO LEARN EACH SECRET CAUSE;
LET NUMBER'S, FIGURE'S, MOTION'S LAWS
     REVEALED BEFORE ME STAND;
THESE TO GREAT NATURE'S SCENES APPLY,
AND ROUND THE GLOBE, AND THROUGH THE SKY,
DISCLOSE HER WORKING HAND.[1]

AKENSIDE was speaking for many poets and versifiers of his age when he wrote his "Hymn to Science." "Born in an age more curious than devout," as Young said, they were as concerned as were philosophers and scientists to pry into the secrets of Nature and to understand her laws. Voltaire might say that the Newtonian system was no proper subject for poetry because of its "Geometry"; such strictures did not deter the English poetasters who in verse—if not in poetry—strove to express "Number's, Figure's, Motion's laws." Even the better poets were not above making the attempt, though on the whole their interest in the *Opticks* was shown less in their versification of the physics of light than in such descriptive technique as we have seen. But the "scientific poets" acknowledged no limitations to the province of poetry. Their interest in the *Opticks* was by no means confined to appreciation of the new beauty which Newton's discoveries had given to "the choir of heaven and the furniture of earth." They would have felt some surprise—and even more disdain—at Wordsworth's later hesitant position con-

[1] Mark Akenside, "Hymn to Science"; *Works*, edited Johnson, Vol. 55, p. 357.

[55]

cerning the "Man of Science" and the "Poet," and his suggestion that, when and if science became intelligible, discoveries of the scientists might become legitimate material for
poetry.[2] To the poets of the eighteenth century the time had
already come for poets to "follow the steps of the Man of
Science"; the "remotest discoveries" of the scientist were to
them "as proper objects of the Poet's art as any upon which
it can be employed"; science, already "familiarized to men,"
had become "a dear and genuine inmate of the household
of man."

I

THEIR modern descendants, like Wordsworth, have forgotten
the scientific poets of the eighteenth century, or if they know
them at all, remember their nonscientific passages. Yet in
their day these works were widely read, as were the encyclopedias of science with which they really belong.[3] There was,
for example, John Reynolds, who proposed to teach the
young the "more noted Phaenomena of Nature" and to
familiarize them with the Newtonian discoveries, who was
quite willing to grant that he was no poet but a mere versifier,[4]
and who showed more interest in his elaborate paraphernalia
of scientific footnotes than in his text. In 1709 he published
the first version of *Death's Vision*; reprinted in 1716 and in
1719, the work appeared in an expanded version as *A View
of Death* in 1725. Examination of the various editions shows
the extent to which popular interest in science was growing.

[2] "Preface to Lyrical Ballads" (1800).

[3] I have selected Reynolds, Blackmore, Brooke, Browne, and Jago from
the many scientific poets of the period, because they show the influence of
the *Opticks* clearly.

[4] In his preface (*A View of Death*, London, 1735, p. xiii) Reynolds
says: "The Critic, no doubt, will spy many transgressions of his laws and
skill. I must confess I could never allow myself to study the laws of
Poetry, or the accuracies of a Poem. I never thought my self naturaliz'd
(for they say, *Poeta nascitur*) that way; or that the rules of art would
supply the defects of nature."

As so often in this kind of poetry, Reynolds used the device of the soul's cosmic voyage, when, released by death, the curious spirit of man might gain empirical knowledge of the air, the ether, the sun, the planets. So tedious are Reynolds' long reflections, together with his careful notes, that we come to agree with him that death was the happiest possible solution for such a soaring soul, which, not content with books, demanded immediate experience of the stars and planets, the ethereal tracts, and the laws of light. Weep not for this Adonais! He desired nothing so much as

> Learn'd death! that in one hour informs me more
> Than all the academic aids could do; . . .
> Than chronics, books, and contemplations too!

We feel that congratulation rather than sympathy is in order as the poetaster hails

> Death! that exalts me strait to high'st degree!
> Commenc'd a more than Newton in abstruse philosophy![5]

Not long after Reynolds published the early edition of *Death's Vision*, Richard Blackmore completed the much more extensive *Creation*, a physico-theology in verse. Perhaps he was immediately inspired by the success of William Derham's lectures of 1711, which in their published form the author entitled *Physico-Theology*, and which, with the companion-volume, *Astro-Theology*, went through edition after edition and remained standard for at least two generations. The ultimate origin of the *Creation*, however, was in Blackmore's desire to oppose the growing power of "atomism." As a physician, well read in many branches of contemporary science, he was fully aware of the important development of scientific atomism, which, particularly under the influence of Gassendi and Boyle, had made great headway in the seventeenth century. But to the poet Blackmore as to many others, Lucretius was less important as a father of modern science than as the

[5] *A View of Death*, p. 45.

expositor of "Epicureanism," that much abused term, which served as a cloak for all excesses, whether of manners or morals. The "Epicureans" were heretics—even more, they were atheists, followers of Hobbes, the Arch-Heretic. As staunchly as the Elder Brother in *Comus*, Blackmore opposed "that power, which erring men call Chance," the fortuitous concourse of atoms. It has long been the fashion to laugh at Blackmore, rather than to read him. He has never recovered from the disservice done him by the Scriblerians. Not even the praise of Dr. Johnson served to counteract the ridicule of Pope. Yet Backmore's imitation of the Lucretius he constantly opposed had made him famous at a time when the youthful Pope was still lisping in numbers, hardly known to fame. As a versification of science, the *Creation* continued to have great prestige, and, indeed, was the source and model of many later poems written by the scientific poets.

Henry Brooke was perhaps the most "scientific" poet of the generation. Who now reads *Universal Beauty*,[6] except in extracts, chosen apparently with a desire on the part of editors to avoid all that made Brooke's poem popular in its generation? Brooke declared that he had set himself a "daring unexampl'd task"; certainly no other poet of the period ventured to crowd into his lines so many complexities, in comparison with which Newton's own technicalities in the *Principia* or the *Opticks* are as clear as the light whose nature he analyzed. Yet Brooke's treatment of the new scientific theories was an able encyclopedia in verse; his notes are often illuminating, and usually more intelligible than his compressed text. And in spite of his technicalities and abstrusities, there is no question that Henry Brooke felt profoundly, and transmitted to his generation his belief that the discoveries of science proved what certain philosophers had only surmised—that there is universal beauty in the works of God.

[6] *Universal Beauty* was published in parts from 1734 to 1736.

Moses Browne's "Essay on the Universe"[7] traced its ancestry back to Fontenelle on the one hand, to Blackmore's *Creation* on the other. When he said in his preface that he knew of none save Blackmore who had ever attempted a poem of this sort, he was conveniently forgetting several of his predecessors. Like Fontenelle, he desired to instruct the weaker intellects, to bring science and philosophy down from the mountaintops, to make it "a genuine inmate of the household of man." He took all knowledge to be his province; like such encyclopedists as Derham, he was concerned with both "astro-theology" and "physico-theology"; like the "excursion" poets, he divided his attention almost equally between the phenomena of earth and the heavens. Somewhat later in the century Richard Jago in *Edge-Hill* followed Reynolds, Blackmore, Brooke, and Browne in an attempt to grasp the whole of things entire. He too embellished his text with trappings of learned footnotes, and while his concern was rather with "philosophia" than with "scientia," science was an inevitable part of his poetry. Such poets as these concerned themselves less with the beauty of color and the splendor of light than with physical and epistemological problems which they believed Newton had solved for his generation.

II

BOTH the versifiers and the poets were greatly interested in recent theories of the speed of light, as indeed they had reason to be, for few more spectacular discoveries have ever been made than that of Römer, who by careful astronomical measurements put an end to the scholastic theory that light is instantaneous by proving its movement and velocity. Others had surmised that light "travels" but no one before Römer had suggested the fantastic rate of that journey. Today even

[7] Moses Browne, "Essay on the Universe," in *Poems on Various Subjects*, London, 1735; my references are to the second edition of the *Poems*, London, 1739.

the layman speaks easily of "millions of light years," but human imagination had never associated such astronomical figures as those proposed by Römer and Cassini with the everyday occurrence of visible objects in the lighted world. As Blackmore said:

> Behold the Light emitted from the Sun,
> What more familiar, and what more unknown;
> While by its spreading Radiance it reveals
> All Nature's Face, it still it self conceals. . . .
> How soon th' Effulgent Emanations fly
> Thro' the blue Gulph of interposing Sky!
> How soon their Lustre all the Region fills,
> Smiles on the Vallies, and adorns the Hills!
> Millions of Miles, so rapid is their Race,
> To cheer the Earth, they in few Moments pass.
> Amazing Progress! At its utmost Stretch,
> What human Mind can this swift Motion reach?[8]

The scientific poets cited Römer, Newton, Huygens, and others. "Mr. Huygens observes," said Browne,[9] "a Bullet discharged from a Cannon, proceeding with an equal Velocity, would be 25 Years in coming from the Sun to us, whereas the Rays of Light, which is a body too, arrive to us from thence in 7 minutes and a half of Time." Reynolds quoted Newton correctly as saying that the rays of light spend "about seven or eight minutes in coming to us from the sun," and added that Dr. Cheyne in the *Philosophical Transactions* estimated that light travels 130,000 miles a second.[10] Small wonder that the Scriblerians, Swift, Pope, and Arbuthnot, suggested as one of the "Discoveries and Works of the Great Scriblerus" a proposal for "a method to apply the Force arising from the

[8] *Creation. A Philosophical Poem*, London, 1715 (third edition), II. 386-399.
[9] "Essay on the Universe," p. 340.
[10] Römer's estimate was closer to the modern figure of 186,000 miles a second.

immense Velocity of Light to mechanical Purposes."[11] The
poets found interest in attempting to describe the speed of
light, and in drawing from it metaphors and similes. "Light
Fancy speeds along, Quick as the darted beam from pole to
pole."[12] "Mysterious Thought . . . who canst distance motion
in thy flight . . . Swifter than light outspeed the flame of
day"[13]; "the vain excursive light, Fleet as the wind, precipitates its flight."[14] Thomson wrote in his poem on Newton:

> Nor could the darting speed of light immense
> Escape his swift pursuit and measuring eye.[15]

Mallett recalled such observers as Römer, who through telescopic observation had proved that light is far from instantaneous:

> the sage, who, studious of the skies,
> Heedful explores these late-discovered worlds,
> By this observed, the rapid progress finds
> Of light itself; how swift the headlong ray
> Shoots from the Sun's height through unbounded space,
> At once enlightening air, and Earth, and Heaven.[16]

Young, in a poem devoted to darkness, did not forget the
"silver chains of light" sent down to man by God and Love.
He too pondered:

> How far, how wide,
> The matchless monarch, from his flaming throne,

[11] *Memoirs of Martinus Scriblerus,* in *Satires and Personal Writings of
Jonathan Swift,* edited W. A. Eddy, London and New York, 1932, p. 136.
In spite of the fact that the *Memoirs* were not published until 1741, and
that they were emended and corrected by Pope, there is no reason that this
particular passage should not have been in the original version made by the
Scriblerians in 1713-14.
[12] David Mallett, *The Excursion*; Chalmers, XIV. 19.
[13] Henry Brooke, *Universal Beauty*; Chalmers, XVII. 338.
[14] Richard Oakley, "Will with a Wisp"; Chalmers, XVI. 258.
[15] "To the Memory of Sir Isaac Newton," ll. 94-95.
[16] David Mallett, *The Excursion*; Chalmers, XIV. 22.

Lavish of lustre, throws his beams about him,
Farther and faster than a thought can fly.[17]

Young and Akenside were only two of several poets who,
in their lines on the speed of light, showed the combination of
new science and old theology in this period. Their imagination
had grown with the "worlds unnumber'd" through which the
God is known; they had no hesitation in accepting the idea of
indefinite cosmic universes throughout space and time; yet
their little world, while responding to natural laws which
they never doubted, was still to them created, as it would end,
in finite time. The light which takes "7 Minutes and a half of
Time" in coming from the sun, many years in coming from
the fixed stars, is nevertheless the same light which God
created in the First Day's Work. "How distant some of these
nocturnal suns," pondered Young,

So distant (says the sage), 'twere not absurd
To doubt if beams, sent out at Nature's birth,
Are yet arrived at this so foreign world;
Though nothing half so rapid as their flight.[18]

Akenside, remembering such chronologies as those of Luther
and Ussher, was even more specific in dating "Nature's
birth" approximately four thousand years before Christ, as
he considered the

fields of radiance, whose unfading light
Has travell'd the profound six thousand years,
Nor yet arrives in sight of mortal things.[19]

Lemuel Gulliver, on the third of his voyages, discovered a
race of men who showed the vacillation between science and

[17] *Night Thoughts*, IX. 1616-1619.
[18] *Ibid.*, IX. 1224-1228.
[19] *Pleasure of Imagination*, I. 204-206. Akenside added a note (first edition, London, 1744, p. 20) : "It was a notion of the great M. Huygens, that
there may be fix'd stars at such a distance from our solar system, as that
their light shall not have had time to reach us, even from the creation of
the world to this day."

[62]

superstition in a different way. The Laputans had far out-distanced their English contemporaries in their mathematical theories, and particularly in their astronomical observations, since they had discovered the moons of Mars two centuries before these were first observed in Europe; yet the Laputans were fearful about the coming of a comet which might upset their world with its tail, and they were so concerned about sun-spots and the dissipation of energy in the sun that their first query in the morning was concerning the sun's health.[20] It was unfortunate that Captain Gulliver had not carried in his pocket such a versified encyclopedia as Reynolds' *View of Death*, by means of which the Laputans might have been able to

> Solve their distracting problems quick and show
> Rules of reflected and refracted light,[21]

and in which they would have found, in both text and notes, a discussion of the apparent self-contradictions in the

> Prodigious source of Life! that e'er since time begun,
> Has wasting still, and undiminish'd run! . . .
> Swift streams! that almost leave the thought behind,
> Almost outfly the sallies of the Mind.[22]

But Reynolds was no more able to explain certain prob-lems of the sun's energy and of the transmission of light than were the Laputans, for on some of these, great men like New-ton, Hooke, Huygens, did not agree, though each had his theory; and other problems of the maintenance of the sun's energy and of the mode and medium of the propagation of light were as mysterious to them as they still remain to mod-ern physicists. Yet, wishful-thinkers as the poets were, they were persuaded that had Newton not been untimely plucked

[20] The background of this satire is discussed in Marjorie Nicolson and Nora Mohler, "Scientific Background of Swift's *Voyage to Laputa*," *Annals of Science*, II (1937), pp. 299-335.

[21] *A View of Death*, p. 44.   [22] *Ibid.*, pp. 51-52.

from them—at the ripe age of eighty-five!—he would have found the answer to all problems. Unfortunately

> embrac'd by th' icy arms of age,
> And his quick thought by time's cold hand congeal'd
> Ev'n Newton left unknown this hidden power.[23]

The eighteenth century poets were as aware of the importance of Newton's observations on sound as are his modern critics, one of whom says[24]: "It may be remarked in passing that Newton's theory of periodic vibrations in an elastic medium, which he developed in connexion with the explanation of sound, would alone entitle him to a place among those who have exercised the greatest influence on the theory of light, even if he had made no direct contribution to the latter subject." Richard Glover said in the eighteenth century:

> O had great Newton, as he found the cause
> By which sound rouls thro' th' undulating air,
> O had he, baffling time's resistless power,
> Discover'd what that subtile spirit is,
> Or whatsoe'er diffusive else is spread
> Over the wide-extended universe,
> Which causes bodies to reflect the light,
> And from their straight direction to divert
> The rapid beams, that through their surface pierce . . .[25]

III

IF THE poets were confused about the propagation of light, they had every reason for their confusion; for not only did the scientists disagree, but Newton himself had vacillated between a wave theory and a corpuscular theory; while he finally committed himself to the latter in the *Opticks*, he did so with evident hesitation, since his chief pronouncements were couched in the form of "Queries," and he went only so

---

[23] Glover, "A Poem on Newton."
[24] E. T. Whittaker, "Introduction" to Newton's *Opticks, ed. cit.,* p. xvii.
[25] Glover, "A Poem on Newton."

far as to suggest that light "might" be transmitted as he suggested.[26] He was entirely candid in his statement about the "Aethereal Medium": "I do not know what this Aether is."[27] Certainly the poets knew much less! Nevertheless, they grappled heroically with problems of the nature of both air and ether, with theories of the transmission of sound and light, and they may be forgiven if they took refuge in mere analogies between sound and light, for did they not have authority here in Newton himself?[28] Confusing—and often confused—as their "authorities" were, it is remarkable that the poets made as much of them as they did. But let them speak for themselves, even though more briefly than they would have wished.

[26] See particularly Queries 17-23 at the end of the *Opticks*.

[27] *Opticks*, Query 18. In a paper sent to the Royal Society in 1675, Newton had postulated "an aetherial medium, much of the same constitution with air, but far rarer, subtiler, and more strongly elastic . . . a vibrating medium like air, only the vibrations far more swift and minute" which pervades the pores of all natural bodies. A full discussion of both the physical and metaphysical ideas of Newton on the ether may be found in Edwin Arthur Burtt, *The Metaphysical Foundations of Modern Physical Science*, New York, 1925, pp. 263-280. (This volume also appeared as *The Metaphysics of Sir Isaac Newton*, London, 1925.) In the *Opticks*, Query 18, Newton said, after discussing certain experiments of Boyle and others on the extraction of air from cylindrical vessels: "Is not the Heat of the warm Room convey'd through the Vacuum by the Vibrations of a much subtiler Medium than Air, which after the Air was drawn out remained in the Vacuum? And is not this Medium the same with that Medium by which Light is refracted and reflected, and by whose Vibrations Light communicates Heat to Bodies, and is put into Fits of easy Reflexion and easy Transmission? . . . And is not this Medium exceedingly more rare and subtile than the Air, and exceedingly more elastick and active? And doth it not readily pervade all Bodies? And is it not (by its elastick force) expanded through all the Heavens?"

[28] Newton was, of course, misled by his analogy between color and the musical chord, probably because of the influence upon him of Kepler's Pythagorean devotion to the ideas of the harmony of the spheres, which is pervasive in Kepler's optical theories. Newton believed that light travels like sound by longitudinal impact of corpuscles that make up the medium. This led him to the conclusion that in the denser medium the light corpuscles would travel faster—a position which was not disproved until the nineteenth century.

Blackmore, writing early, had less opportunity than later poets to find alternative theories of the propagation of light brought conveniently together and interpreted. Then, too, in this period the deification of Newton had not begun, and many scientists were still inclined to opposing hypotheses. While Blackmore knew the Newtonian theories of light, he was less impressed by the *Opticks* than by the *Principia*, which is central to his thinking in *Creation*.[29] In his discussion of the transmission of light, he concerned himself almost entirely with air rather than with ether. Various conclusions of Boyle about the "elastic air" were in his mind as they were in Newton's:

> Remark the Air's transparent Element,
> Its curious Structure, and its Vast Extent;
> Its wondrous Web proclaims the Loom Divine,
> Its threads the Hand that drew them out so fine. . . .
> Let curious Minds, who would the Air inspect,
> On its Elastic Energy reflect;
> The secret Force thro' all the Frame diffus'd,
> By which its Strings are from Compression loos'd,
> The spungy Parts, now to a straighter Seat
> Are forc'd by Cold, and widen'd now by Heat.[30]

In his long discussion of the transmission of light, Blackmore seems to have been studying the *Opticks* carefully; his order is largely that of Newton's in Queries 17-22; he deals, at least casually, with nearly all the problems raised by Newton. But whether because of a happy guess, or because of some

[29] Blackmore frequently paid tribute to

> The Masters form'd in Newton's famous School,
> Who do the Chief in modern Science rule,
> Erect their Schemes by Mathematick Laws,
> And solve Appearances with just Applause. (Book II, p. 57)

If Blackmore seems to sidestep Newton's corpuscular theory of light it may well have been because the theory seemed to him to approach too closely to atomism.

[30] *Creation*, II. 618-641.

authority whom he was opposing to Newton, he put his finger upon a weak spot in Newton's armor in his lines immediately following those on the speed of light:

> But if, to save so quick a Flight, you say,
> The ever-rolling Orb's impulsive Ray
> On the next Threads and Filaments does bear,
> Which form the springy Texture of the Air,
> That these still strike the next, till to the Sight
> The quick Vibration propagates the Light;
> 'Tis still as hard, if we this Scheme believe
> The cause of Light's swift Progress to conceive.[31]

Reynolds, however, was a thoroughgoing Newtonian. In brief passages he introduced Newton's corpuscles, as well as the theory that light travels in straight lines unless refracted or inflected:

> What natures now, what shapes these atoms wear,
> That form this fluid, this elastick air!
>   Atoms too fine for former light
> But large and gross to incorporeal sight. . . .
> Swift streams! that almost leave the thought behind,
> Almost outfly the sallies of the Mind.
> Sagacious they! that still unerring tend
> The shortest way to their designed end!
> Sure to come there, while nothing can repress
> Their speedy flight, but unresisting emptiness.[32]

Brooke's discussion in *Universal Beauty* is the most exact treatment in verse of the period. He too began with the nature of the air:

> For while the circumambient air we sing,
> Its springy tension and elastic spring;

[31] *Ibid.*, II. 400-407. Blackmore was sound here in his belief that Newton's corpuscular theory of the transmission of light by impact—as happens in the propagation of sound in air—would slow up the velocity of light, and would not agree with the velocity through the ethereally filled spaces between the heavenly bodies, such as the sun and the earth.

[32] *A View of Death*, pp. 17, 51.

The quick vibration of the yielding mass,
How objects through its lucid medium pass;
For Nature how the smiling glass expands;
Narcissus-like, how beauteous Nature stands,
Self-lov'd within the splendid mirror shines,
But self-enjoy'd, nor like Narcissus pines.[33]

In another passage, he was less rhetorical and more technical:

The subtile mass its copious mantle spreads,
Its mantle wove of elemental threads;
Th' elastic flue of fluctuating air,
Transfus'd invisible, enfolds the sphere;
With poinance delicate pervades the whole,
Its ear, eye, breath, and animating soul.[34]

Later he proceeded to a versification of Newtonian theories of the reflection, refraction, and inflection of light:

How, as a talisman of magic frame,
This atmosphere conveys th' enlight'ning beam,
Reflects, inflects, refracts the orient ray;
Anticipating sheds the rising day—
High from his seat the solar glory heaves,
(Whose image fires the horizontal waves)
Abridging, shears the sable robe of night,
And through the globe protracts the cheerful light;
With sweet preambling twilight blends the shade,
And gently lets our evening beam recede.[35]

[33] *Universal Beauty*, II. 33 ff.; Chalmers, XVII. 341.
[34] *Ibid.*, I. 352 ff.; Chalmers, p. 340.
[35] *Ibid.*, II. 41 ff.; Chalmers, pp. 340-341. In justice to Brooke, his careful notes should be considered with the text, for the notes afford an excellent example of "science for the layman" in this period. I quote only his note on this particular passage: "Its still more wonderful quality, in not only reflecting, but refracting, and inflecting the morning and evening beam; in appearance, lifting the Sun about four degrees above his station, and refracting the light to us when the Sun is about eighteen degrees below the horizon; by which means our day is prolonged about two hours, and the tedious night in the frigid zones shortened annually about thirty-two days."

From his consideration of light "for the benefit and use of man," Brooke turned to other problems of the physics of light:

> Thus, borne on airy wings, the radiance flies,
> Quickening the vision of poetic eyes:
> Whence we may pierce into the deep profound,
> And, searching, view the wondrous system round:
> For wide as universal Nature spreads,
> Light's sacred fount its streaming lustre sheds;
> Still orient, to the parting beam succeeds;
> Through azure climes a sumless journey speeds;
> Its restless longitude the glory darts,
> Nor less a boundless latitude imparts;
> Where matter borders on retiring space,
> Impulsive urges the perpetual race;
> Stupendous length, illimited by aught
> Of numbers summ'd or multiply'd by thought![36]

To the ultimate problem of the source of this great energy which fills the universe, Brooke could reply only as Newton himself believed:

> But whence the light's invigorating force,
> Its active energy, or secret source,
> Must be ascribed to that Eternal Spring,
> Whom first, and last, and ever bless'd we sing—
> Who only could his effluent angel send;
> Athwart the gulf the radiant blaze extend;
> Kindle the mass to incorporeal speed;
> The flame with never-dying splendours feed;
> With heat the universal page unseal;
> With light the universal charm reveal;
> In prospect wide th' illustrious work display,
> And gem the pavement of the milky-way;
> Make grace from use, and use from beauty flow;
> With florid pencil, shade the jasper bow.[37]

[36] *Ibid.*, II. 51 ff.; Chalmers, p. 342.
[37] *Ibid.*, II. 65 ff.

IV

BECAUSE of their exactness and laborious care, the scientific poets, while they instructed, could hardly be said to delight. The descriptive poets, equally interested in the new theories, but not unduly concerned to teach them, succeeded better in translating the Newtonian physics of light into poetry. Mallett and Thomson were probably as widely read in contemporary science as was Brooke, and their knowledge of the physics of the *Opticks* was as sound; yet they concerned themselves less with versifying the laws than with attempting to describe light as it appears to man on earth. Mallett in the second book of *The Excursion* implied all that Blackmore, Reynolds, and Brooke have said, yet transmuted their metal into something finer as he beheld the "innumerous streams Flow lucid forth, and roll through trackless ways":

> The fountain-orb . . . expands immense.
> A shoreless sea of fluctuating fire,
> That deluges all ether with its tide.
> What power is that, which to its circle bounds
> The violence of flame! in rapid whirls
> Conflicting, floods with floods, as if to leave
> Their place, and, bursting, overwhelm the world!
> Motion incredible! to which the rage
> Of oceans, when whole winter blows at once,
> In hurricane, is peace. But who shall tell
> That radiance beyond measure, on the Sun
> Pour'd out transcendent! those keen-flashing rays
> Thrown round his state, and to yon worlds afar
> Supplying days and seasons, life and joy!
> . . . Yet not all alike
> Resplendent; in these liquid regions pure,
> Thick mists, condensing, darken into spots
> And dim the day. . . . Dilated some and dense,
> Broad as Earth's surface each, by slow degrees
> Spread from the confines of the light along,
> Usurping half the sphere, and swim obscure

On to its adverse coast; till there they set,
Or vanish scatter'd; measuring thus the time
That round its axle whirls the radiant orb.
Fairest of beings! first-created light!
Prime cause of beauty![38]

"Prime cause of beauty," light as the source of color and light in itself. As the Newtonian theories had shown poets new beauty in gems, in the rainbow, in the succession of colors in the day, as it had caused them to watch with more discerning eyes the successions of light and color from early dawn until nightfall, so it produced a new awareness of light observed apart from color. We see this in Thomson's comet and his meteors; we feel it in Young and other poets who preferred night to day. We find the new awareness of light in many descriptions of the Milky Way, even more exact— and much more involved in light—than those of the seventeenth century whose poets were the first to translate this phenomenon into verse:

The milky way, whose stream of vivid light,
Pour'd from innumerable fountains round
Flows trembling, wave on wave, from sun to sun,
And whitens the long path to Heaven's extreme.[39]

During the seventeenth century descriptions of the moon had taken on new realism, thanks to Galileo's telescope, but the eighteenth century moon shows, as it were, still another phase:

[38] *The Excursion*, II. pp. 21-22.
[39] *Ibid.*, p. 23. Milton's lines (*Paradise Lost*, VII. 577-581), poetically the finest written after Galileo's discoveries, do not suggest as great consciousness of light:

A broad and ample road, whose dust is gold,
And pavement stars, as stars to thee appear
Seen in the Galaxy, that milky way
Which nightly as a circling zone thou seest
Powdered with stars.

Now dance the stars, where Vesper leads the way;
Yet all faint-glimmering with remains of day.
Orient, the Queen of Night emits her dawn,
And throws unseen, her mantle o'er the lawn.
Up the blue steep, her crimson orb now shines;
Now on the mountain-top her arm reclines,
In a red crescent seen: Her zone now gleams
Like Venus, quivering in reflecting streams,
Yet reddening, yet round-burning up the air,
From the white cliff, her feet slow-rising glare!
See! flames condens'd now vary her attire;
Her face, a broad circumference of fire.
Dark firs seem kindled in nocturnal blaze;
Through ranks of pines, her broken lustre plays,
Here glares, there brown-projecting shade bestows,
And, glittering, sports upon the spangled snows.[40]

In this age, more curious than devout, even the glowworms
and fireflies which gleam through so much of the night-
poetry caused men to ponder on the Newtonian theories of
light, as a minor poet suggested, watching the "will with a
wisp":

Profuse, the living particles of fire,
Which, from her lap, the Earth prolific flings, ..
Some, lightly mounting in th' etherial sky,
Expatiate freely, and in meteors fly[41];
Some, near the ground, their vagrant course pursue,
And blend delusion with the nightly dew:
For whether from the strife of moist and dry,
Or from bitumen fiery sparkles fly,
A sudden flame the mingling vapours give,
Which seems, to mortal eyes, to move and live.
Lo! when the beauteous landscape fades in night,

[40] Richard Savage, *The Wanderer*, ed. cit., pp. 35-36.
[41] The term "meteor," as will be seen here and in other quotations, was
used very loosely in the eighteenth century. Meteors were supposed to be
productions from terrestrial causes, and their origin was frequently explained by such causes as Oakley here suggests.

In some irriguous valley, glimmering bright,
The false flame dances, or with quivering gleam,
Skims on the bosom of the wandering stream. . . .
Now through the void the vain excursive light,
Fleet as the wind, precipitates its flight.[42]

The "moral" of this slight poem may serve as conclusion to the discussion of attempts on the part of eighteenth century poets to versify the Newtonian physics of light:

Descartes thus, great Nature's wandering guide,
Fallacious led philosophy aside,
'Till Newton rose, in orient beauty bright,
He rose, and brought the world's dark laws to light,
Then subtle matter saw, and vanished at his sight.

For a moment we look before and after, as we find the *ignis fatuus* leading to a tribute to Newton: we look backward to the attempts—sometimes clumsy—to express what Pope said succinctly in his epitaph on Newton; we look forward to a much more difficult problem—the extent to which, in the minds of both philosophers and popular writers, the Newtonian physics became involved with the supposed Newtonian epistemology, aesthetics, and metaphysics.

[42] Richard Oakley, "Will with a Wisp"; Chalmers, XVI. 258. The poem is given among the works of Francis Fawkes, but according to Fawkes' note, it was written by his tutor, the Reverend Richard Oakley, former fellow of Jesus College, Cambridge. Fawkes translated it from the original Latin.

CHAPTER FOUR

OPTICS AND VISION

LET NEWTON, PURE INTELLIGENCE, WHOM GOD
TO MORTALS LENT TO TRACE HIS BOUNDLESS WORKS
FROM LAWS SUBLIMELY SIMPLE, SPEAK THY FAME
IN ALL PHILOSOPHY.[1]

EWTON himself would regret the fact that ever since his death he has been considered a metaphysician. Influenced though he was by philosophy from his Grantham school days when he came under the influence of Henry More and the Cambridge Platonists, Newton was never a philosopher and did not aspire to such distinction. Indeed, he would have preferred the proud title "theologian" to that of either "philosopher" or "scientist." Vehement opposition to his early optical ideas led him for a time to consider giving up both science and philosophy. "I intend," he wrote to Oldenburg, "to be no further solicitous about matters of Philosophy; and therefore I hope you will not take it ill, if you find me never doing anything more in that kind."[2] Hypotheses, he insisted, were not to be regarded in experimental philosophy; certainly his introduction to the *Opticks*, in its curt brevity and succinctness, was intended to absolve him from any intention of proceeding from physics to metaphysics: "My Design in this Book is not to explain the Properties of Light by Hypotheses, but to propose and prove them by Reason and Experiments."[3] There is little enough metaphysics in Newton's scientific writings, and students have

[1] James Thomson, "Summer," ll. 1560-1563.
[2] Quoted *Opticks*, edited Whittaker, *ed. cit.*, p. xv.
[3] *Opticks*, Book I, Part I; *ed. cit.*, p. 1.

been forced to deduce many of his philosophical opinions from his letters. Indeed, one of his most acute modern critics writes:

> Would that in the pages of such a man we might find a clear statement of the method used by his powerful mind in the accomplishment of his dazzling performances . . . or an exact and consistent logical analysis of the ultimate bearings of the unprecedented intellectual revolution which he carried to such a decisive issue! But what a disappointment as we turn the leaves of his works! Only a handful of general and often vague statements about his method, which have to be laboriously interpreted and supplemented by a painstaking study of his scientific biography. . . . In scientific discovery and formulation Newton was a marvellous genius; as a philosopher he was uncritical, sketchy, inconsistent, even second-rate.[4]

But because of Newton's pre-eminence in science, the concluding passages of the *Principia* and the purposely hesitant "Queries" appended to the *Opticks*, which Newton intended as tentative and not final statements, were seized upon as absolute verities by an age to which Newton had offered so much in the way of scientific proof that the generation insisted on finding in his pronouncements the final expression of ultimate realities. The initial approach to the supposed philosophy of Newton may best be made by way of a consideration of the physics of sight, with particular reference to the optics of the eye, which will lead to both physical and metaphysical problems of vision and to epistemology.

I

EARLY in the seventeenth century Francis Bacon had found it strange that the "form and origin of light" had been so

---

[4] E. A. Burtt, *Metaphysical Foundations of Modern Physical Science*, p. 203. A still more valuable study, so far as the *Opticks* is concerned, is Elsie C. Graham, *Optics and Vision: The Background of the Metaphysics of Berkeley*, n.p., 1929.

little inquired into, and urged such inquiry upon his country-
men. In his own time, however, the fundamental bases of
both optics and vision were being laid by Kepler. For centuries men had remained content with vague surmises of the
Greeks, who in their optical theories had concerned themselves with "the science of sight, never, in the modern sense,
of light. Light [was], for the Greeks, not something in itself,
but the means of sight; not something to be considered apart,
but as a condition of the visible. There are plenty of light
theories in ancient thought—though they are not to be found
in its optics—but they are at bottom not so much theories of
light as of perception."[5] To the Pythagoreans, sight, like
sound, was something which emanated from the organs of
seeing or hearing; to the Atomists sight and sound were
caused by an efflux from the object. Even as late as the seventeenth century, both theories were still pervasive, particularly
among poets.[6] Plato combined the two,[7] holding that vision
is "caused by something emanating from the eye and coales-
cing with the object." Upon one or two occasions Aristotle
agreed, declaring that in vision "it is the diaphanous, as e.g.
the air, which is stimulated by colour, and the sense-organ is
stimulated by this contiguous medium."[8] More characteristic,
however, was Aristotle's insistence in the *Metaphysics* that
vision is to the organs of sight as thinking is to the living
body, functions of energizing matter; if the whole body were
an eye, then its soul would be vision. Specifically Aristotle
held with Democritus that the essential element in the eye is

[5] Elsie Graham, *Optics and Vision*, p. 14.

[6] Gretchen Finney of Smith College has made an interesting collection
of passages in sixteenth and seventeenth century literature in which sound
is still described as emerging from the ear, according to the Pythagorean
tradition.

[7] *Meno*, 76 C; *Timaeus*, 45; cf. Graham, *Optics and Vision*, p. 14.

[8] *De Anima*, Part 2, Chapter 7; *Parva Naturalia*, Chapter 2.

water, and that "sight is reflected from air and any object with a smooth surface, just as it is from water."[9]

Ptolemy went further than had any of the classical Greeks in combining the problems of light and sight, but it remained for the Arabian Alhazen to lay the basis for modern thought in both optics and vision. Systematized and interpreted by his thirteenth century disciple Vitellio, the theories of Alhazen, finally published as the *Thesaurus Opticae,* remained standard until late in the sixteenth century, when Maurolycus made the discovery that the crystalline humour of the eye is a lens. In a period when, by means of telescopic and microscopic lenses, astronomers were discovering a new universe of the great, biologists a new world of the minute, it was inevitable that investigation of the lens of the eye and theories of vision should proceed by leaps and bounds. Kepler brought together all the important earlier findings in optics, to which he added discoveries of his own. Descartes went further, as did a half-dozen lesser thinkers in the pre-Newtonian period. Basic principles of the science of optics were laid; metaphysical problems of vision and perception were raised if not finally answered. Physics and metaphysics became so inextricably interwoven that Newton found it essential to discuss both in his "Queries."

II

ONE important chapter in the development of optics has been deliberately omitted from this brief survey of important stages in pre-Newtonian optics, because the camera obscura forms the best possible transition from technical theories of scientists to the imaginative response of laymen. The invention of this "pretty thing" is often ascribed to Giambattista della Porta, but, while Porta popularized it in the sixteenth century, the principle was known much earlier. Euclid seems to have used something of the sort; so too did Alhazen and

---

[9] *Meteorologica,* 372 B; cf. Graham, pp. 17-18.

Roger Bacon. Leon Battista Alberti, the painter, made use of such a device in an exhibition in 1437. Leonardo da Vinci, that myriad-minded man, reached conclusions on the structure of the eye in connection with the principle of the camera. In 1521—before Porta's birth—the first published account appeared in the *Architecture* of Vitruvius. Like the early telescope, the camera obscura seemed to some of its first users only a pleasant novelty; but resemblances to the principle of human vision had occurred to various thoughtful men before Kepler developed the analogies more fully. Familiar as is Sir Henry Wotton's letter,[10] parts of it will bear repetition. Writing to Francis Bacon in December 1620, he told of a visit to Kepler, and of a "draft of a landscape on a piece of paper, methought masterly done," which to Wotton's momentary bewilderment Kepler declared that he himself had made "non tanquam pictor, sed tanquam mathematicus." Wotton then described the "little black tent . . . which he can suddenly set up where he will . . . exactly close and dark, save at one hole, about an inch and a half in diameter, to which he applies a long perspective trunk, with a convex glass fitted to the said hole, and the concave taken out at the other end . . . through which the visible radiations of all the objects without are intromitted, falling upon a paper . . . and so he traceth them with his pen in their natural appearance." Wotton felt some reservations about the artistic integrity of using the camera obscura; but with his scientific interest, he could see other values: "This I have described to your Lordship, because I think there might be good use made of it for chorography; for otherwise to make landscapes by it were illiberal, though surely no painter can do them so precisely." The serious use which Kepler made of the camera is too well known to need repetition. It was a model of the eye, a visible evidence of the method by which vision takes place. Kepler had surmised the

10 *Life and Letters of Henry Wotton*, edited Logan Pearsall Smith, Oxford, 1907, II. 205-206.

appearance of the actual image upon the retina; it remained only for Christopher Scheiner to prove the surmise, which he did by experiments first upon the eyes of animals, then on human eyes. He cut away the coats of the back parts of eyes of sheep and oxen, and, holding objects before them, saw the images of the objects clearly and distinctly inverted upon the naked retina. His exhibition of the experiment at Rome in 1625 provoked great interest and excitement.

Laymen like Wotton, philosophers like Bacon, scientists like Kepler, found equal interest in the camera obscura, which was used by both "pictor" and "mathematicus." A few references by eighteenth century writers will be sufficient to indicate the continued popular interest. Addison in his *Pleasures of the Imagination*, discussing "nature" and "art," said:

> We may be sure that artificial works receive a greater advantage from their resemblance of such as are natural; because here the similitude is not only pleasant, but the pattern more perfect. The prettiest landscape I ever saw, was one drawn on the walls of a dark room, which stand opposite on one side to a navigable river, and on the other to a park. The experiment is very common in optics.[11]

After describing the miniature scenes as they appeared on the walls, Addison concluded: "I must confess, the novelty of such a sight may be one occasion of its pleasantness to the imagination, but certainly the chief reason is the near resemblance to nature, as it does not only, like other pictures, give the colour and figure but the motion of the thing it represents." The poets, too, were charmed by this early "moving picture." John Gay, admiring the miniature scenes upon a lady's exquisite fan, wrote:

> Thus have I seen woods, hills, and dales appear,
> Flocks graze the plains, birds wing the silent air,
> In darken'd rooms, where light can only pass

[11] *Spectator* 414.

Through the small circle of a convex glass;
On the white sheet the moving figures rise,
The forest waves, clouds float along the skies.[12]

Walter Harte in his "Essay on Painting" suggests the interest of an eighteenth century painter in the principle of the camera :

So Vandervaart in later times excell'd,
And nature liv'd in what our eyes beheld.
He too can oft (in optics deeply read)
A noon-day darkness o'er his chamber spread;
The transient objects sudden as they pass
O'er the small concave of the visual glass,
Transferr'd from thence by magic's powerful call,
Shine in quick glories on the gloomy wall;
Groves, mountains, rivers, men surprise the sight,
Trembles the dancing world, and swims the wavy light.[13]

Among the remarkable applications of new scientific theories which the Hermit exhibited to Savage's Wanderer was an adaptation of the camera obscura, which at first glance seems almost to imply that the images which entered the Hermit's cave came straight from Heaven!

My labour yon high-vaulted altar stains
With dies, that emulate aetherial plains.
The convex glass, which in that opening glows,
Mid circling rays, a pictured Saviour shows!
Bright it collects the beams, which, trembling all,
Back from the God, a showery radiance fall.[14]

The ultimate significance of the camera obscura to the philosopher and the layman will appear in the future. It is enough for the present to stress the fact that here was visible evidence—which even the poet could understand—of the process by which the external world is "painted" on the

[12] "The Fan"; Chalmers, X. 442.
[13] "An Essay on Painting"; Chalmers, XVI. 323.
[14] *The Wanderer, ed. cit.*, p. 23.

human eye. Few men save physiologists could observe what Scheiner saw in the dead eyes of animals; but the layman could begin to appreciate that miracle which occurs daily as man goes about "seeing" the external world through eyes which cannot choose what they will see, but which are the chief intermediary between "mind" and "matter." To the thoughtful man of any generation, sight is at once the most natural and the most mysterious of all connections between man and nature. The child and the "rude swain" take it for granted; but once we begin to ponder the problem of how we know the external world, we—like our predecessors in the seventeenth and eighteenth centuries—find ourselves involved in metaphysics or epistemology.

III

IT WAS natural that in this period sight should have been exalted even more than before as the supreme sense. So, indeed, it is, although most of us take it for granted. If we or those close to us are deprived of it, we come to understand the rebellion of the blind poet against physical laws which confine sight and light to one organ:

> O first-created Beam, and thou great Word,
> "Let there be light, and light was over all,"
> Why am I thus bereaved thy prime decree?
> The Sun to me is dark
> And silent as the Moon,
> When she deserts the night,
> Hid in her vacant interlunar cave.
> Since light so necessary is to life,
> And almost life itself, if it be true
> That light is in the soul,
> She all in every part, why was the sight
> To such a tender ball as the eye confined,
> So obvious and so easy to be quenched,

And not, as feeling, through all parts diffused,
That she might look at will through every pore?[15]

There were, of course, many reasons for the immense popularity of Milton in the eighteenth century; but perhaps one minor one was that this generation became so much more sympathetically aware than men had ever been of what blindness implied in divorcing man from external nature.

Sight, to Locke,[16] as to Descartes, was "the most comprehensive of all our senses, conveying to our minds the ideas of light and colours, which are peculiar only to that sense; and also the far different ideas of space, figure, and motion, the several varieties whereof change the appearances of its proper object, *viz.*, light and colours." To Berkeley,[17] sight was "the most noble, pleasant, and comprehensive of all the senses." To Addison it was the one essential sense on which imagination rests:

> Our sight is the most perfect and most delightful of all our senses. . . . The sense of feeling can indeed give us a notion of extension, shape, and all other ideas that enter at the eye, except colours; but at the same time it is much straitened and confined. . . . Our sight seems designed to supply all these defects, and may be considered as a more delicate and diffusive kind of touch, that spreads itself over an infinite multitude of bodies. . . . We cannot indeed have a single image in the fancy that did not make its first entrance through the sight.[18]

Philosophers, scientists, laymen, all showed great interest in the problems of a "man born blind," which William Molyneux raised, and which became a commonplace of the generation. Milton had lost his sight in maturity; but what of a man

[15] *Samson Agonistes*, ll. 83-97.

[16] *Essay Concerning Human Understanding*, Book II, Chapter IX, section 4; in *Works*, edited St. John, London, 1876, I. 257. Aristotle had said that vision was the most important organ of knowledge.

[17] *A New Theory of Vision*, in *Essay, Principles, Dialogues of Berkeley*, edited Mary Whiton Calkins, New York, 1929, Introduction, p. 5.

[18] *Spectator* 411.

born blind, who gained sight after he had reached years of reason? Would his former tactual response to such geometrical forms as a cube and cylinder prove the same as his visual response when he saw the objects for the same time? Molyneux's interest in the problem was not entirely objective; his wife had lost her sight, and he was struggling with personal problems of the blind. His first mention of the blind man to Locke was in a letter, which Locke quoted in the *Essay*[19]; later Molyneux went into the matter more fully in his *Dioptrica Nova*, published in 1692. Berkeley, taking his point of departure in part from Locke and in part from his countryman Molyneux, discussed the blind man in *A New Theory of Vision*, saying that "a man born blind, being made to see, would at first have no idea of distance by sight. . . . The objects intromitted by sight would seem to him (as in truth they are) no other than a new set of thoughts and sensations."[20] Molyneux's blind man was cited by Locke as proof of his belief of the extent to which man is "beholden to experience, improvement, and acquired notions." Later in the *Essay* Locke used an illustration of the limitations of another blind man who, no matter what his ancestry, produced different progeny than did Molyneux's character:

> To hope to produce an idea of light or colour by a sound, however formed, is to expect that sounds should be visible, or colours audible. . . . Which is all one as to say, that we might taste, smell, and see by the ears: a sort of philosophy worthy only of Sancho Panza, who had the faculty to see Dulcinea by hearsay. . . . A studious blind man, who had mightily beat his head about visible objects, and made use of the explication of his books and friends, to understand those names of light and colours which often came in his way, bragged one day, That now he understood what scarlet signified. Upon which his

[19] Book II, Chapter IX, section 8.
[20] *New Theory*, section 41, *ed. cit.*, pp. 33-34, 61, 63-65. See also *passim*, since Berkeley remained much interested in the problem of the blind man.

friend demanding what scarlet was? The blind man answered,
It was like the sound of a trumpet.[21]

Popularized in *Tatler* 227, the blind man who "heard" red
became a familiar figure in the eighteenth century and may
be found in Fielding, Watts, Johnson, and others.[22]

Steele was responsible for adding still another blind man
to the procession which crosses the pages of popular writers
in the eighteenth century. In *Tatler* 55 he told the story of
William Jones of Newington Butts, who, born blind, gained
sight at the age of twenty. Had Addison popularized this
particular tale, he would probably have paid more attention
to Molyneux's and Locke's blind man, with his cubes and
cylinders. But Steele preferred the human to the scientific in-

[21] Book III, Chapter IV, section 11.

[22] The literary history of this blind man is traced by Kenneth MacLean
in *John Locke and English Literature of the Eighteenth Century*, New
Haven, 1936, pp. 106 ff. But the blind man who gave rise to so much
popular discussion in the period was no single individual. Steele in *Tatler*
55, discussed below, is talking about still another person; and Swift's
"man born blind," who in the third book of *Gulliver's Travels* was able to
distinguish colors by touch, had a different origin. Mr. MacLean's surmise that Swift was here satirizing such current theories as those of
Locke was entirely natural. When I was working upon "The Scientific
Background of *The Voyage to Laputa*," I also took for granted that this
blind man was "general" satire of the period and interpreted him in terms
drawn from Molyneux, Locke, and Newton. As Miss Nora Mohler and I
discovered more and more specific sources for Swift's supposed "general"
satire, I became suspicious about the "man born blind"; by a lucky chance,
one of us stumbled upon his specific source in Boyle's *Works*, where
Boyle tells the exact story, related to him by a friend, about an Italian
blind man who was said to have such power as Swift implies. Swift's
satire in *The Memoirs of Martinus Scriblerus, ed. cit.*, p. 135, in which
Scriblerus was said to have this power, went back to the general background of Molyneux, Locke, and particularly Newton: The "Great Scriblerus . . . by the delicacy of his Touch, could distinguish the different
Vibrations of the heterogeneous Rays of Light." Later in the period, as
Mr. MacLean points out, there enters another important blind man, in the
person of the English mathematician, Nicholas Saunderson, who also was
believed capable of distinguishing colors by touch. But as Boswell reports
in his account of one of Johnson's conversations (*Life*, edited G. B. Hill, II.
218), Saunderson realized that such discrimination was impossible.

terest. True, he quoted the attending surgeon as urging by-standers not to assist the youth, but to "let the patient make his own observations, without the direction of any thing received by his other senses," but he was chiefly interested in the emotional responses of the young man, his mother, and his fiancée. This tale, like that of Molyneux's blind man and Locke's character who saw scarlet in terms of a trumpet-sound, persisted in literature for many years. In such a poem as William Thompson's "Sickness," we find some reminis-cence of these accounts, though Thompson was describing not a man born blind but one who, through illness, had tem-porarily lost the sense of sight:

> Heavens! is the day restor'd
> To my desiring eyes? their lids, unglew'd,
> Admit the long-lost sight, now streaming in
> Painfully clear! O check the rapid gleam
> With shading silk, 'till the weak visual orb,
> Stronger and stronger, dares imbibe the sun.[23]

The most complete treatment in eighteenth century poetry of the many themes of the "man born blind" may be found in a long passage in *Edge-Hill* in which Jago versified the Steele story, adding careful discussion of the patient's visual re-sponse to objects which he had previously known only through other senses; here Steele, Molyneux, Locke, and various writers on optics and vision were brought together into a single whole.[24]

Newton's persistent interest in the "harmony" of color and sound—his heritage doubtless from the Pythagorean strain so marked in Kepler—afforded additional evidence to those who believed that the blind might "see" color in terms of sound. On several occasions in the *Opticks* he had developed

[23] "Sickness"; Chalmers, XV. 51.
[24] Chalmers, XVII. 298-300. I am not quoting various other literary treatments of the theme, since Mr. MacLean has included several in his study.

mathematical similarities between certain color-rings and the chord: "There, where the Rings are successively made by the limits of the seven Colours, red, orange, yellow, green, blue, indigo, violet in order . . . are to one another as the Cube Roots of the Squares of the eight lengths of a Chord, which sound the Notes in an eighth, *sol, la, fa, sol, la, mi, fa, sol.* . . ."[25] Most of all, in his "Queries," he said:

> May not the harmony and discord of Colours arise from the proportions of the Vibrations propagated through the Fibres of the optick Nerves into the Brain, as the harmony and discord of Sounds arise from the proportions of the Vibrations of the Air? For some Colours, if they be view'd together, are agreeable to one another, as those of Gold and Indigo, and others disagree.[26]

The "clavecin" or "colour-organ," invented by Père Louis Bertrand Castel, exhibited in France in 1735 and in London in 1757, was an attempt to prove that the deaf might "see the music of the ears," the blind "hear the music of the eyes," while normal men "who have both eyes and ears will enjoy music and colors better by enjoying them both at the same time."[27] The classical tale of Memnon's harp was revived in poetry with new significance, since it well illustrated both the relationship between light and sound which existed in nature, and the equally mysterious yet natural relationship between faculties of man's mind and external nature:

> As Memnon's marble harp, renown'd of old
> By fabling Nilus, to the quivering touch

[25] *Opticks* (first edition), Book II, Part I, Observation 14.

[26] *Ibid.*, Book III, Part I, Query 14; *ed. cit.*, p. 346.

[27] Castel's invention is discussed by Erika von Erhardt-Siebold in "Some Inventions of the Pre-Romantic School and Their Influence upon Literature," *Englische Studien*, LXVI. 3 ff., and by the same author in "Harmony of the Senses in English, German, and French Romanticism," *P.M.L.A.*, XLVII (1932), 577 ff. In the second article Mrs. von Erhardt-Siebold discusses the interest of the Romanticists in figures of speech mingling two or more senses.

Of Titan's ray, with each repulsive string
Consenting, sounded thro' the warbling air
Unbidden strains; ev'n so did nature's hand
To certain species of external things,
Attune the finer organs of the mind:
So the glad impulse of congenial pow'rs,
Or of sweet sound, or fair-proportion'd form,
The grace of motion, or the bloom of light,
Thrills thro' imagination's tender frame,
From nerve to nerve: all naked and alive
They catch the spreading rays: till now the soul
At length discloses every tuneful spring,
To that harmonious movement from without,
Responsive.[28]

The increasing self-consciousness of the eighteenth century about the sense of sight led to a growing interest in all the senses, their processes, and their interrelationship, and to an awareness of the "harmony of the senses" familiar in the Romanticists. In *Pleasures of the Imagination* Addison had suggested the enhancement of the sense of sight by impressions of other senses:

As the fancy delights in everything that is great, strange, or beautiful, and is still more pleased the more it finds of these perfections in the same object, so it is capable of receiving new satisfaction by the assistance of another sense. Thus any continued sound, as the music of birds, or a fall of water, awakens every moment the mind of the beholder, and makes him more attentive to the several beauties of the place that lie before him. Thus if there arises a fragrancy of smells or perfumes, they heighten the pleasure of the imagination, and make even the colours and verdure of the landscape appear more agreeable; for the ideas of both senses recommend each other, and are pleasanter together than when they enter the mind separately.[29]

[28] Akenside, *Pleasures of Imagination*, I. 109-124.
[29] *Spectator* 412.

Akenside in theory expounded the idea, Thomson in practice developed it. Akenside versified Addison, stressing more poetically the harmony of the senses:

> The sweets of sense,
> Do they not oft with kind accession flow,
> To raise harmonious fancy's native charm?
> So while we taste the fragrance of the rose,
> Glows not her blush the fairer? While we view
> Amid the noontide walk a limpid rill
> Gush through the trickling herbage, to the thirst
> Of summer yielding the delicious draught
> Of cool refreshment; o'er the mossy brink
> Shines not the surface clearer, and the waves
> With sweeter music murmur as they flow?[30]

Thomson walked through the country, his senses all responsive:

> Oft let me wander o'er the dewy fields
> Where freshness breathes, and dash the trembling drops
> From the bent bush, as through the verdant maze
> Of sweet-briar hedges I pursue my walk;
> Or *taste the smell of dairy*; or ascend
> Some eminence, Augusta, in thy plains,
> And see the country, far-diffused around,
> One boundless blush, one white-empurpled shower
> Of mingled blossoms; where the raptured eye
> Hurries from joy to joy.[31]

As he walked, he realized more acutely than ever before the limitations of the poetical vocabulary of his time to express the harmony of the senses to which poets themselves were responding even more than in the past:

> Ah, what shall language do? ah, where find *words*
> *Tinged with so many colours* and whose power,
> To life approaching, may *perfume my lays*

[30] Akenside, *Pleasures of Imagination*, II. 73-83.
[31] "Spring," ll. 103-112.

With that fine oil, those aromatic gales
That inexhaustive flow continual round?[32]

Yet the dominant interest of the poets, as of their philosophical predecessors, continued to be in

Sight, all-expressive! Tho' the feeling sense
Thrills from Ianthe's hand; at Handel's lyre,
Tingles the ear; tho' smell from blossom'd beans
Arabian spirit gathers; and the draught
Sparkling from Burgundy's exalted vines
Streams nectar on the palate; yet O Sight!
Weak their sensations when compared with thee.
Without thee Nature lies unmeaning gloom.
Whatever smiles on Earth, or shines in Heav'n,
. . . all are thine.[33]

IV

"THRO' chinks, styl'd organs, dim life peeps at light," said
Young.[34] But how is the contact between "dim life" and the
external world attained? It was all very well for the night-
poet to speak glibly of "chinks, styl'd organs," or in another
mood to write:

[32] Ibid., ll. 475-479. I stop over these few illustrations because there is
still a tendency to consider the realization of the "harmony of the senses"
a prerogative of the Romantic poets. I am sure that Thomson, Akenside,
Mallet, Jago, and many others would have been surprised at this kind of
estimate (Erika von Erhardt-Siebold, "Harmony of the Senses," *ed. cit.*,
p. 583) : "We realize, of course, that the eighteenth century had deliberately repressed the individual life of the senses; and that whenever we find
attempts at imparting some individual idea of the life of the senses, the
poetic feeling seems frustrated by the conventional expression, by the
analytic-objective way of presentation. The eighteenth century did not
comprehend that subtle quickening of a single sense impression, still less
of several sense impressions." The eighteenth century poets were certain
that theirs was the first generation which had ever discovered the life of
the senses!
[33] William Thompson, "Sickness"; Chalmers, XV. 51.
[34] *Night Thoughts*, III. 450.

O what a confluence of ethereal fires,
From urns unnumber'd, down the steep of Heaven,
Streams to a point, and centres in my sight![35]

This might do for rhetoric; but it failed to answer the question: How does vision occur? Although the poets were less concerned with the physical problems of optics than with the metaphysical relationship between man and his world, they were as scientifically minded as they were philosophically inclined, and willing to grapple with physical problems which led to better comprehension of the epistemological. Indeed, it is a mark of men's interest in these questions and an indication of their importance to human beings that, as a group, the poets refused to take either of two easy ways out of their dilemma. One way was offered by Young himself. Having sought answers to recurrent questions of his period in philosophy, science, and theology, and "found no end in wandering mazes lost," he declared on this particular problem: it is enough for man that he possesses the miracle of sight; his not to reason why; his but to accept with gratitude what Nature has given:

Who sees, but is confounded, or convinc'd?
Renounces reason, or a God adores?
Mankind was sent into the world *to see*:
Sight gives the science needful to their peace;
That obvious science asks small *learning's* aid.
Wouldst thou on metaphysic pinions soar?
Or wound thy patience amid logic thorns?
Or travel history's enormous round?
Nature no such hard task enjoins; she gave
A make to man directive of his thought;
A make set upright, pointing to the stars,
As who should say: "Read thy chief lesson there!"[36]

But to the majority of poets of the eighteenth century, this was the way of the child who had not reached years of

[35] *Ibid.*, IX. 749-751.   [36] *Ibid.*, IX. 859-870.

reason, the "rude swain" who ran to catch the rainbow's glory, the "sequacious herd" which feared because it did not understand the comet. More characteristic was the attitude expressed by Jago:

> The vulgar race of men, like herds that graze,
> On instinct live, not knowing how they live:
> While reason sleeps, or waking stoops to sense.
> But sage philosophy explores the cause
> Of each phenomenon of sight, or sound,
> Taste, touch, or smell; each organ's inmost frame,
> And correspondence with external things:
> Explains how diff'rent texture of their parts
> Excites sensations diff'rent, rough, or smooth,
> Bitter, or sweet, fragrance, or noisome scent:
> How various streams of undulating air,
> Through the ear's winding labyrinth convey'd,
> Cause all the vast variety of sounds.
> Hence too the subtle properties of light,
> And sev'n-fold colour are distinctly view'd,
> In the prismatic glass, and outward forms,
> Shown fairly drawn, in miniature divine,
> On the transparent eye's membraneous cell.[37]

No; Young's way out would not do for these poets; and, more curious still, they did not make use of the still easier way of satire. The Age of Newton was, after all, the greatest age of English satire, against which little proved sacred. Yet one of the most interesting facts which emerges from this study is that Newton was taken so seriously—even reverently—that he remained above and beyond satire. Philosophers and philosophical systems were the meat and drink of satirists: Descartes was damned with impunity; Hobbes had laid himself open to the attacks he received; Locke, revered by many, nevertheless might lead to laughter—except in so far as his theories were interpreted as Newtonian exposition;

[37] *Edge-Hill*, Book III; Chalmers, XVII. 298.

Berkeley was often legitimate prey when he was noticed at all by popular writers. But the "godlike Newton" remained somehow apart, beyond evil, beyond satire. Because of the high seriousness which marks most of the poetic treatments of the *Opticks*, it is a passing relief to a modern irreverent mind to find at least one poet who dared have fun with current theories of perception and vision—though he was satirizing Descartes rather than Newton. Prior, writing *Alma* in prison in 1715, was able to explain clearly how sight occurs:

> Two optic nerves, they say, she ties,
> Like spectacles, across the eyes;
> By which the spirits bring her word,
> Whene'er the balls are fix'd or stirr'd. . . .
> Without these aids, to be more serious,
> Her power, they hold, had been precarious.[38]

In place of the complicated theories of perception offered to his generation, he proposed a system which, had it been widely adopted, would have put a convenient end to the knotty problems we are here considering:

> My simple system shall suppose
> That Alma enters at the toes;
> And then she mounts by just degrees.

But there is little of this in the period of deification of Newton. The popular writers might and did disagree with their idol; but they did so respectfully and not satirically.

The poets were willing—indeed, they were eager—to put themselves to school to the modern "master of them that know," who had taken the place of honor so long reserved for Aristotle. If, in order to understand the Newtonian epistemology, they must first grasp the Newtonian optics, they were no less willing to do so than they had been to study the Newtonian physics of light. If the student of literature wishes to see the extent to which technicalities of the optics of vision

[38] Matthew Prior, *Alma*; Chalmers, X. 193.

came to be taken for granted as a part of the education of the
intelligent "lady" and "gentleman" of the day, let him turn
to the translation of Fontenelle's perennially popular *Plurality
of Worlds*, made by "a Gentleman of the Inner Temple" who
in the mid-eighteenth century brought Fontenelle's somewhat
antiquated science up to date.[39] Here he will find a long section, added to the "Fourth Evening," discussing in highly
technical detail the science of optics. Newton's discoveries
and theories were set forth, illustrated by plates and diagrams, with an exposition of the physics and physiology of
optics, and a glossary of new scientific terms which ladies
and gentlemen were evidently supposed to know. Popular
writers referred easily to the "Tunica Cornea" and the
"Tunica Retina"; they had much to say of pictures "painted"
on the eye; they were familiar with the findings of such experimental scientists as Scheiner and his successors; they
were aware of the lenslike function of the "crystalline humour."

> Who form'd the curious texture of the eye,
> And cloath'd it with the various tunicles,
> Of texture exquisite; with chrystal juice
> Supply'd it, to transmit the rays of light?

So Henry Needler[40]; Henry Brooke as usual went further in
his discussion, implying the geometry of vision, which, stem-
ming from Kepler and Descartes, had been taken for granted
and further developed by Newton:

> With conscious act the vivid semblance vies,
> And subtle now the sprightly nerve supplies;
> Unconscious lifts the lucid ball to light,

[39] *Conversations on a Plurality of Worlds . . . A New Translation . . .
with great Additions. Extracted from the best modern Authors, on many
Curious and Entertaining Subjects . . . By a Gentleman of the Inner
Temple.* London, 1760; see particularly pp. 218-264.
[40] Henry Needler, "A Poem to Prove the Certainty of a God," reprinted in *Miscellaneous Correspondence*, edited Benjamin Martin, London,
1759, I. 235-236.

And glares around with unperceiving sight. . . .
So temper'd wondrous by mechanic scheme,
The Sovereign Geometrician knits the frame;
In mode of organizing texture wrought,
And quick with spirited quintessence fraught;
When objects on the exterior membrane press,
The alarm runs inmost through each dark recess,
Impulsive strikes the corresponding strings,
And moves th' accord of sympathetic springs.[41]

V

NEWTON had showed that, as even the layman knew from the camera obscura, "pictures" of external objects are "lively painted" on the "thinner Coats" of the eye, and that "these Pictures, propagated by Motion along the Fibres of the Optick Nerves into the Brain, are the cause of Vision." He discussed—as had Kepler, Descartes, Molyneux, and others before him—a persistent problem: Why, having two eyes, upon the retina of each of which the inverted image of an object is "painted," do we ordinarily see "single" rather than "double"?[42] "Accordingly as these Pictures are perfect or im-

[41] *Universal Beauty*, IV. 32-44; Chalmers, XVII. 351. Needler and Brooke, together with many other poets, were following Newton's discussion, *Opticks*, Book I, Part I, Axiom VII. (I omit his various references to the diagrams which accompanied this section.) ". . . the Light which comes from the several Points of the Object is so refracted by the transparent skins and humours of the Eye, (that is, by the outward coat . . . called the *Tunica Cornea*, and by the crystalline humour . . . which is beyond the Pupil . . .) as to converge and meet again in so many Points in the bottom of the Eye, and there to paint the Picture of the Object upon that skin (called the *Tunica Retina*) with which the bottom of the Eye is covered. For Anatomists, when they have taken off from the bottom of the Eye that outward and most thick Coat called the *Dura Mater*, can then see through the thinner Coats, the Pictures of Objects lively painted thereon. And these Pictures, propagated by Motion along the Fibres of the Optick Nerves into the Brain, are the cause of Vision."
[42] Discussion of the various theories on this matter may be found in Elsie Graham, *Vision and Optics*. Newton offers his explanation in *Opticks*, Book III, Part I, Query 15.

perfect, the Object is seen perfectly or imperfectly," Newton said in the passage following immediately his discussion of the "cause of Vision." The layman is always interested in scientific explanations of "imperfect" vision which touches his experience closely. The poets showed their familiarity not only with Newton's theories, but also with their further development in the *New Theory of Vision*, in which Berkeley offered more specific causes for both "faint" and "confused" vision. Among the causes of imperfect vision, Newton had mentioned such diseases as jaundice, the decay of the eye through old age, shortsightedness and farsightedness—or, in his own terminology, the visual conditions of men "whose Eyes are too plump" and others suffering from "the defect of plumpness in the Eye."[43] Berkeley concerned himself with different problems[44]: Clear vision occurs when the rays proceeding from an object "are, by the refractive power of the crystalline, accurately reunited in the retina"; if they are reunited either before or after they arrive at the retina, confusion results; such "confused vision" attends near objects and is different from "faint vision," which attends remote objects: "Faint vision is when, by reason of the distance of the object, or grossness of the interjacent medium, few rays arrive from the object to the eye. This is opposed to vigorous or clear vision, and attends remote objects."

Several of the descriptive poets referred to theories of imperfect vision. Savage, for instance, noticed, in connection with lightning, that "a dire deception strikes the mental eye"[45]; he observed a "meteor"—that term which he and others used broadly:

> Full-orb'd it shone, and dimm'd the swimming sight,
> While doubling objects danc'd with darkling light.[46]

[43] Book I, Part I, Axiom VII; *ed. cit.*, pp. 14-16.
[44] *A New Theory of Vision*, sections 30-40; the discussion precedes Berkeley's treatment of the "man born blind."
[45] *The Wanderer, ed. cit.*, p. 27.   [46] *Ibid.*, p. 54.

The night-poets frequently spoke of both "faint" and "confused" vision. But of all the poets, Thomson was not only the most interested in such problems of imperfect vision, but the most accurate in his observations. Like Newton, he mentioned the effect of jaundice: "The yellow-tinging plague Internal vision taints"[47]; he introduced into serious poetry a familiar cause of "double vision," when in "Autumn" he described an evening's jollity which went too far until

> Their feeble tongues,
> Unable to take up the cumbrous word,
> Lie quite dissolved. Before their maudlin eyes,
> Seen dim and blue, the double tapers dance,
> Like the sun wading through the misty sky.
> Then, sliding soft, they drop. Confused above,
> Glasses and bottles, pipes and gazeteers,
> As if the table even itself was drunk. . . .[48]

In the early editions of "Summer," he suggested the effect upon man's senses of excessive light and heat:

> The too resplendent scene
> Already darkens on the dizzy eye,
> And double objects dance.[49]

One of Thomson's best descriptions of "faint vision" occurred on an evening in summer, when the "Glow-worm lights his gem; and through the dark, A moving radiance twinkles":

> A faint erroneous ray,
> Glanced from the imperfect surfaces of things,
> Flings half an image on the straining eye; ·

[47] "Spring," ll. 1083-1084. The figurative association of jaundice and jealousy, which Thomson is here using, is probably as old as jaundice itself. But the suggestion that jaundice "taints" the "internal vision" is, I think, Newton's.

[48] "Autumn," ll. 552-558.

[49] The lines appeared in the 1727 edition (cf. *Complete Poetical Works*, *ed. cit.*, p. 122). They continued to appear in the editions from 1730 to 1738, with one slight, but significant, change: instead of "dizzy eye," Thomson wrote, more accurately, "dizzy sight."

While wavering woods, and villages, and streams,
And rocks, and mountain-tops that long retained
The ascending gleam are all one swimming scene,
Uncertain if beheld.[50]

He experienced "confused vision" in autumn fog, when the
sun "sheds, weak and blunt, his wide refracted ray":

Indistinct on earth,
Seen through the turbid air, beyond the life
Objects appear, and, wildered, o'er the waste
The shepherd stalks gigantic; till at last,
Wreathed dun around, in deeper circles still
Successive closing, sits the general fog
Unbounded o'er the world.[51]

As figures of speech, the ideas of "imperfect," "weak,"
and "confused" vision served the poets well, permitting them
to express familiar ideas in slightly different language, and
draw old morals from new materials. Pope used "imperfect
vision" twice in the First Epistle of the *Moral Essays*, once
in connection with the "dream psychology" standard in the
period:

As the last image of that troubled heap,
When Sense subsides, and Fancy sports in sleep,
(Though past the recollection of the thought)
Becomes the stuff of which our sleep is wrought:
Something as dim to our internal view,
Is thus, perhaps, the cause of most we do.
True, some are open, and to all men known;

[50] "Summer," ll. 1687-1693.
[51] "Autumn," ll. 724-730. Cf. Pope, *Dunciad*, I. 79-80:

All these, and more, the cloud-compelling queen
Beholds through fogs, that magnify the scene.

An interesting example of the psychological effect of "imperfect vision"
may be seen in the early version of Thomson's meteor-passage, originally
given in entirety in the 1727 version of "Summer," transferred, with re-
visions, to "Autumn" in 1730. The original is given by Robertson, *ed. cit.*,
pp. 131-132.

Others so very close, they're hid from none;
(So Darkness strikes the sense no less than Light).[52]

In another figure in the same Epistle, he deftly combined
several of the current technicalities of optics and vision:

the diff'rence is as great between
The optics seeing, as the objects seen.
All Manners take a tincture from our own;
Or come discolour'd through our Passions shown.
Or Fancy's beam enlarges, multiplies,
Contracts, inverts, and gives ten thousand dyes.[53]

Indeed the poets of the Age of Newton found theories of
optics and vision peculiarly apt for application to familiar
antitheses: for generations light had been equated with Reason; old ideas of the passions could be fitted neatly into the
new theory of color refracted from light. Both were important, even essential; yet pure light was the source of
ultimate truth—as it had always been—while light "discolour'd through our Passions" afforded a nice rhetorical
variant for expressing an old idea. So too the antithesis between Reason and Fancy could be readily expressed in terms
of modern optics, since Fancy responded to "imperfect,"
"faint," "confused" sight, while Reason always saw clearly.
Akenside was particularly fond of this kind of figure:

deluded long
By fancy's dazzling optics, these behold
The images of some peculiar things,
With brighter hues resplendent, and portray'd
With features nobler far than e'er adorn'd
Their genuine objects.[54]

In his discussion of conduct and ethics, he suggested that
"where fancy cheats the intellectual eye, With glaring colours and distorted lines,"[55] man is easily led astray, but

[52] *Moral Essays,* Epistle I. 45-53.   [53] *Ibid.,* I. 31-36.
[54] *Pleasures of Imagination,* III. 152-157.   [55] *Ibid.,* II. 29-30.

                    where the pow'rs
Of fancy neither lessen nor enlarge
The images of things, but paint in all
Their genuine hues, the features which they wore
In nature; there opinion will be true
And action right.[56]

These are rhetorical figures, to be sure; but this was more
than rhetoric to Akenside and his generation; here, as elsewhere, Newton's scientific discoveries afforded new ammu-
nition to ethical poets; the Newtonian metaphysics, because
of its Neo-Platonism, easily led to an imputation of ethical
values to nature.

VI

IN THE twenty-eighth "Query" of the *Opticks* Newton himself passed momentarily from physics to metaphysics. At
present we shall consider only two sentences: "How came the
Bodies of Animals to be contrived with so much Art, and for
what ends were their several Parts? Was the Eye contrived
without Skill in Opticks, and the Ear without knowledge of
Sounds?"[57] There was, of course, nothing novel in these
questions; philosophy and religion had always asked and
answered them according to their times and presuppositions.
But the rapid development of the sciences had made them
even more acute; and the growing tendency toward atomism
had served to render the metaphysics and ethics of the "Epicurean heresy" even more dangerous than in the past. Chance
and the fortuitous concourse of atoms must be opposed by
Design, and Plan, most of all by "Creative Wisdom." It is
perhaps significant that Newton introduced his brief disquisition on design and plan and the order and beauty of the
universe just where he did—between a lengthy discussion of
matter, and his longest treatment of the corpuscular theory

[56] *Ibid.*, III. 18-23.
[57] *Opticks*, Book III, Query 28; *ed. cit.*, pp. 369-370.

of light, both of which approached too closely to atomism for the comfort of the orthodox.

Prior could dismiss the "Lucretian heresies" with laughter:

> Note here, Lucretius dares to teach
> (As all our youth may know from Creech)
> That eyes were made, but could not view,
> Nor hands embrace, nor feet pursue:
> But heedless Nature did produce
> The members first, and then the use.[58]

Blackmore, however, considered the challenge of the old Epicureanism and the new scientific atomism so serious that he devoted all the books of the *Creation* to disproving them:

> With Thought from Praepossession free, reflect
> On Solar Rays as they the Sight respect.
> The Beams of Light had been in vain display'd,
> Had not the Eye been fit for Vision made:
> In vain the Author had the Eye prepar'd
> With so much Skill, had not the Light appear'd.[59]

Trained as a physician, Blackmore knew much more than did intelligent laymen about the structure of the human body; some of his best reasoning in the *Creation* is found in those sections in which he seems to anatomize the body under a microscope, finding in its "design and plan" the final evidence of craftsmanship of the Great Anatomist who made it. He opposed to the Epicureans the miracle of the human eye:

> Lucretians, next regard the curious Eye,
> Can you no Art, no Prudence, there descry?
> By your Mechanic Principles in vain
> That Sense of Sight you labour to explain.[60]

In opposition to the principle of chance, upheld, he believed, by modern atomists no less than ancient, he propounded phys-

---

[58] Matthew Prior, *Alma*; Chalmers, X. 194.
[59] *Creation*, II. 408-413.
[60] *Ibid.*, VII. 112-115.

ical questions frequently raised in the period from Alhazen to Newton:

> But can corporeal Forms with so much Ease
> Meet in their Flight a thousand Images,
> And yet no Conflict, no Collisive Force
> Break their thin Texture, and disturb their Course?
> What fix'd their Parts, and made them so cohere,
> That they the Picture of the Object wear?
> What is the Shape, that from a Body flies?
> What moves, what propagates, what multiplies
> And paints one Image in a thousand Eyes?
> When to the Eye the crowding Figures pass,
> How in a Point can all possess a Place,
> And lye distinguish'd in such narrow Space?[61]

Henry Brooke was no less concerned than was Blackmore to defend modern theories of sight and vision against chance; indeed, in *Universal Beauty*, as in the *Creation*, opposition to "Lucretian heretics" was central to the author's purpose:

> Not thus he gave our optic's vital glance,
> Amid omniscent art, to search for chance,
> Blind to the charms of Nature's beauteous frame;
> Nor made our organ vocal, to blaspheme.[62]

"You taught me language, and my profit on't is—I know how to curse." The reverent writers of the eighteenth century, looking through Nature up to Nature's God, would not arraign their Deity as Caliban his demigod.

Nor would they grant (though they might imply) that God and Nature had erred from their "gracious end" in giving man exactly the kind of optics and the degree of vision he possessed. "Why has not man a microscopic eye?" asked Pope, in terms familiar to his century; he replied succinctly: "For this plain reason, Man is not a fly":

[61] *Creation, ed. cit.*, VII. 122-133.
[62] *Universal Beauty*, V. 33-36; Chalmers, XVII. 357.

Say what the use, were finer optics giv'n,
T' inspect a mite, not comprehend the heav'n?
Or touch, if tremblingly alive all o'er
To smart and agonize at every pore?
Or quick effluvia darting through the brain,
Die of a rose in aromatic pain?
If nature thunder'd in his op'ning ears,
And stunned him with the music of the spheres,
How would he wish that Heav'n had left him still
The whisp'ring Zephyr, and the purling rill?[63]

It was inevitable that, as the microscopical discoveries of Leeuwenhoek, Swammerdam, and many lesser men became involved with new theories of optics and vision, man, fascinated by the world of the minute beyond the naked eye, should question why God had denied him the kind of vision He had given to lesser animals. Locke and Berkeley labored these questions; they are implicit in Newton. Pope's fly, which was probably Locke's, Thomson's "critic fly," which came to him from Berkeley, played their part in indicating the growing popular awareness of metaphysical implications of the new optical theories; but they are so familiar and have been so frequently discussed[64] that we may let them flutter back to join the many other insects pondered over by this age. Pope in his way, Thomson in his, agreed with Blackmore, with Brooke and many others:

Let no presuming impious railer tax
Creative Wisdom, as if aught was formed
In vain, or not for admirable ends.
Shall little haughty Ignorance pronounce
His works unwise; of which the smallest part
Exceeds the narrow vision of her mind?[65]

[63] *Essay on Man,* I. 195-204.
[64] See Kenneth MacLean, *John Locke and English Literature,* pp. 166 ff.; Alan McKillop, *Background of Thomson's Seasons,* pp. 51 ff.
[65] James Thomson, "Summer," ll. 318-323.

"Was the Eye contrived without Skill in Opticks, and the Ear without Knowledge of Sounds?" Newton had asked in the passage which has already been quoted. Briefly he suggested, after his discussion of how man "sees," the problem of how God "sees." In order to understand why Newton felt it necessary to enter into this matter, let us go back to consider certain questions raised by laymen, no less than by scientists and philosophers, about sight and perception. Blackmore may serve as a point of departure. In the section in which he bade the Lucretians "regard the curious Eye," he discussed one of the chief problems of vision: it was all very well to say that the experimental scientists had shown man how he "sees"; but had they explained to man how he "perceives"?

> Since all Perception in the Brain is made,
> (Tho' where and how was never yet display'd)
> And since so great a distance lies between
> The Eye-ball, and the Seat of Sense within,
> While in the Eye th' arrested Object stays,
> Tell, what th' Idea to the Brain conveys?[66]

This was a problem with which Kepler, Descartes, Molyneux, Locke, Newton, had all struggled, and which served as the point of departure for Berkeley, not only in his *New Theory of Vision*, but in his later philosophical works. Even though such observations as those of Scheiner had shown that the inverted image of an object is actually reflected upon the retina, and even though the crystalline humour of the eye had been proved to be a lens, such scientific discoveries and observations failed to answer fundamental questions. Our cameralike eyes "see" miniature inverted pictures; yet we "perceive" more than two-dimensional figures. We *seem* to see

[66] *Creation*, VII. 134-139. Miss Graham in *Optics and Vision* has discussed in detail the physical and metaphysical theories of vision and perception of pre-Newtonian thinkers, as well as the theories of Newton, Locke, and Berkeley.

not only color and shape, but distance, magnitude, relationship. "All Perception in the Brain is made," Blackmore said, but added: "Tho' where and how was never yet display'd." Complex theories had been suggested to answer the question which Blackmore raised: granted that optical experiments had discovered how sight occurs in the eye, yet still "a distance lies between the Eye-ball, and the Seat of Sense within." Even suppose that scientists and philosophers had given a satisfactory answer to the physical problem of the means by which "images" on the retina of the eye are transferred to the "Brain"—what then? Allow these images to be transferred from the eye to the brain by means of the "optick Nerve," as Newton and others had suggested—still, what then? This is only to shift the photograph from one part of man's body to another; it still leaves the "images" imprinted upon matter—whether on the matter of the retina or the matter of the brain:

> Has matter more than motion? Has it thought,
> Judgment and genius? is it deeply learn'd
> In mathematics? has it fram'd such laws,
> Which, but to guess, a Newton made immortal?[67]

Do we explain our perception of visual objects any better by pushing them back from the eye into the brain, if by "brain" we mean merely another material part of the human body? Very well; let us change the terminology, and use the word "mind." We shall not have made real progress in the problem of simple location, but we shall have rid ourselves of a troublesome word; and as Bacon said, while men believe that their understanding governs words, words too often impose upon the understanding. Let us go further, and avoiding the controversies which raged about the "brain" and the "mind," adopt instead Newton's characteristic term, "Sensorium,"

---

[67] *Night Thoughts*, IX. 1475-1478. The passage is here quoted out of its context.

leaving philosophers and scientists to determine the relationship between the sensorium, the brain, and the mind. Newton said:

> Is not the Sensory of Animals that place to which the sensitive Substance is present, and into which the sensible Species of Things are carried through the Nerves and Brain, that there they may be perceived by their immediate presence to that Substance?[68]

From the "Sensory" of animals, he proceeded to the "Sensorium" of Deity:

> Does it not appear from Phaenomena that there is a Being incorporeal, living, intelligent, omnipresent, who in infinite Space, as it were in his Sensory, sees the things themselves intimately, and thoroughly perceives them, and comprehends them wholly by their immediate presence to himself: Of which things the Images only carried through the Organs of Sense into our little Sensoriums, are there seen and beheld by that which in us perceives and thinks.[69]

Addison, responsive as he was to all the intellectual currents of the day, and more responsible than any other popular writer for reading Newton into Locke and Locke into Newton, popularized Newton's idea in an essay on the "Omniscience and Omnipresence of God":

> Several moralists have considered the creation as the temple of God. . . . Others have considered infinite space as the receptacle, or rather, the habitation of the Almighty; but the noblest and most exalted way of considering this infinite space, is that of Sir Isaac Newton, who calls it the sensorium of the Godhead. Brutes and men have their *sensoriola*, or little sensoriums, by which they apprehend the presence, and perceive the actions of a few objects that lie contiguous to them.[70]

[68] *Opticks*, Book III, Part I, Query 28; *ed. cit.*, p. 370.
[69] *Ibid.* Cf. the "General Scholium" to the *Principia*.
[70] *Spectator* 565.

God's Sensorium is everywhere: God is, Addison concludes, "an organ to Omniscience." Man sees in a mirror darkly reflections of reality; God sees face to face, perceives all, realizes all. To an even greater extent than Newton and Addison intended, such a conception of the complete awareness of God's Sensorium served to emphasize still more man's limited and partial experience through his *sensoriola*. God is Pure Light; man's light is refracted, reflected, inflected.

"Of this Truth we may be assured," Molyneux said, "that He that made the Eye shall see."[71] An age more curious than devout—perhaps; but never did an age need God for a final explanation of its philosophy and science more than did the Age of Newton.

[71] William Molyneux, *Dioptrica Nova*, Part I, Proposition XXVIII.

CHAPTER FIVE

AESTHETIC IMPLICATIONS
OF THE OPTICKS

MIND, MIND ALONE, BEAR WITNESS, EARTH AND HEAV'N!
THE LIVING FOUNTAIN IN ITSELF CONTAINS
OF BEAUTEOUS AND SUBLIME.[1]

THE extent to which Newtonian theories of color and light in the *Opticks* affected the theory or technique of painters is a question which lies beyond the scope of this study. Certainly Newton himself showed a good deal of interest in problems of mixing colors, in differences between artificial colors and those of the spectrum, particularly in differences between "whites" produced artificially and the "white" of light. As in their descriptive writing the poets showed themselves studying colors in nature in an attempt to describe them more accurately, so they became more self-conscious about color and light as used by painters, and often expressed their tributes in Newtonian terms.[2] Thus Christopher Pitt wrote to Sir James Thornhill:

Th' exalted strokes so delicately shine,
And so conspire to push the bold design;
That in each sprightly feature we may find
The great idea of the master's mind,
As the strong colours faithfully unite,
Mellow to shade, and ripen into light.[3]

[1] Mark Akenside, *Pleasures of Imagination*, I. 481-483.
[2] In reading through the various collections which I used in preparing this study, I noticed in passing a good deal of this sort of thing, but noted only a few instances of it, since it seemed at the time less significant for my purposes than other treatments of the Newtonian theories.
[3] "To Sir James Thornhill"; Chalmers, XII. 376. The poem was written

Savage's tribute "To Mr. John Dyer, a Painter," included these lines:

> Such vivid tinctures sure through aether glow,
> Stain summer clouds, or gild the watery bow: . . .
> Still stream your colours rich with Clio's rays! . . .
> Clear, and more clear, your golden genius shines,
> While my dim lamp of life obscure declines:
> Dull'd in damp shades, it wastes, unseen, away,
> While yours, triumphant, grows one blaze of day.[4]

James Cawthorn, like various other poets, used the relationship between color and light to point a moral:

> Passions, like colours, have their strength and ease,
> Those too insipid, and too gaudy these:
> Some on the heart, like Spagnoletti's, throw
> Fictitious horrours, and a weight of woe;
> Some, like Albano's, catch from ev'ry ray
> Too strong a sunshine, and too rich a day;
> Others, with Carlo's Magdalens, require
> A quicker spirit, and a touch of fire. . . .
> Wouldst thou then reach what Rembrandt's genius knew,
> And live the model that his pencil drew,
> Form all thy life with all his warmth divine,
> Great as his plan, and faultless as his line;
> Let all thy passions, like his colours, play,
> Strong without harshness, without glaring gay.[5]

Various of the poets, as we have seen, were groping toward what might be called an aesthetic of color and light, but Thomson and Akenside here, as elsewhere, went beyond their contemporaries.

in 1718; the last two lines may be an imitation of Pope's lines (quoted above, p. 9).

[4] *Works*, edited Johnson, Vol. 45, pp. 128-129.

[5] James Cawthorn, "The Regulation of the Passions"; Chalmers, XIV. 242-243.

I

In the Preface to the second edition of "Winter," after discussing the relation between poetry and "the most charming power of imagination," Thomson said:

> I know no subject more elevating, more amusing; more ready to awake the poetical enthusiasm, the philosophical reflection, and the moral sentiment, than the works of Nature. Where can we meet with such variety, such beauty, such magnificence? All that enlarges and transports the soul! What more inspiring than a calm, wide survey of them? In every dress nature is greatly charming—whether she puts on the crimson robes of the morning, the strong effulgence of noon, the sober suit of the evening, or the deep sables of blackness and tempest! How gay looks the Spring! how glorious the Summer! how pleasing the Autumn! and how venerable the Winter!—But there is no thinking of these things without breaking out into poetry.[6]

In his phrases, "such variety, such beauty, such magnificence," Thomson was probably paraphrasing Addison's familiar distinction in *Pleasures of the Imagination,* "the great, the new, the beautiful," as did various other poets who developed the Addisonian categories in their poetry. So, too, Addison's ideas may have been in Thomson's mind when, in his tribute to Newton, he stressed the fact that Newton's wisdom had called forth "from a few causes such a scheme of things, Effects so *various, beautiful,* and *great.*" In *Pleasures of the Imagination,* Addison had associated color with "the beautiful":

> There is a second kind of beauty which we find in the several productions of art and nature, which does not work in the imagination with that warmth and violence as the beauty that appears in our proper species, but is apt, however, to raise in us a secret delight, and a kind of fondness for the places or objects in which we discover it. This consists either in the gaiety

[6] *Complete Poetical Works, ed. cit.,* pp. 240-241. The Preface continued to be printed with successive editions of the poem until 1730.

and variety of colours, in the symmetry and proportion of parts, in the arrangement and disposition of bodies, or in a just mixture and concurrence of all together. Among these kinds of beauty the eye takes most delight in colours. . . . For this reason we find the poets, who are always addressing themselves to the imagination, borrowing more of their epithets from colours than from any other topic.[7]

Addison was aware of the Newtonian discoveries, and elsewhere stressed various of their implications. Yet, although he equated *color* with *beauty*, he seems to have felt little association of *light* with the *sublime*.[8]

Thomson's distinction between "color" as "beautiful," and "light" as "sublime" is shown more fully in his practice than in his theory; yet it is implied in phrases in the Preface already quoted: "How gay looks the Spring! how glorious the Summer!" It is even more clear in the "Hymn on the Seasons," first published in 1730, included in all succeeding versions in the author's lifetime:

These, as they change, Almighty Father! these
Are but the varied God. The rolling year
Is full of thee. Forth in the pleasing Spring
Thy *beauty* walks, thy *tenderness* and *love*.
Wide flush the fields; the softening air is balm;
Echo the mountains round; the forest smiles;
And every sense, and every heart, is joy.
Then comes thy *glory* in the Summer-months,
With light and heat refulgent. Then thy sun
Shoots full perfection through the swelling year:
And oft thy voice *in dreadful thunder* speaks. . . .[9]

[7] *Spectator* 412.
[8] The use of the word "sublime" here is, I realize, inexact, since Addison himself carefully refrained from using it in connection with the effects of external objects upon the imagination. In my forthcoming book I have considered in detail the general background of the "sublime" and "beautiful" in this period; in this limited section, I am using the words as they have been used since Burke.
[9] "A Hymn on the Seasons," in *Complete Poetical Works, ed. cit.*, p. 245. The italics in these passages are mine.

"Spring" is filled with color; "Summer" with light. It is in "Spring" that we are most conscious that "moist, bright, and green, the landscape laughs around." "Spring" is the season in which garden-colors are most vivid:

> At once arrayed
> In all the colours of the flushing year,
> By Nature's swift and secret-working hand,
> Thy garden glows. . . .[10]

In this season the poet shows us the colors of the rainbow, of "broken clouds, gay-shifting to his beam,"[11] of flowers in an English garden,[12] colors everywhere in nature, when "undisguis'd by mimic art, she spreads Unbounded beauty to the roving eye." Thomson's "roving eye" in spring was constantly on the watch for color: "where the raptured eye Hurries from joy to joy,"[13] he saw "the country, far-diffused around One boundless blush."[14] As he found himself incapable of describing the spring flowers "with hues on hues expression cannot paint,"[15] so he indicated the general poverty of poetic vocabulary when it attempted to describe color:

> Behold yon breathing prospect bids the Muse
> Throw all her beauty forth. But who can paint
> Like Nature? Can imagination boast
> Amid its gay creation, hues like hers?
> Or can it mix them with that matchless skill,
> And lose them in each other, as appears
> In every bud that blows? If fancy then
> Unequal fails beneath the pleasing task,
> Ah, what shall language do? ah, where find words
> Tinged with so many colours?[16]

"Spring" is mild, lovely, charming, delightful; it has in it little terror; upon it the poet lavished all the soft—even lush—adjectives of poets at all times. Spring is the creation of

[10] "Spring," ll. 95-98.   [11] Ibid., l. 191.   [12] Ibid., ll. 516 ff.
[13] Ibid., ll. 111-112.   [14] Ibid., ll. 109-110.   [15] Ibid., l. 554.
[16] Ibid., ll. 467-476.

Deity, yet in a sense very familiar in the eighteenth century, the creation less of the awful, radiant, effulgent God who reigns in "darkness visible," than of the Second Person of the Trinity, the kind, humane, tender aspect which God shows His followers in His Son:

> Chief, lovely Spring, in thee and thy soft scenes,
> The smiling God is seen.[17]

In "Summer" we find ourselves in a different world. Here the poet is concerned not only with light, but with excess of light. Even in the moderate climate of England, when the "sun looks in boundless majesty abroad," there enters into *The Seasons* the perennial pleasure-pain theory, of which Burke was to make so much; as "vertical, the sun Darts on the head direct his forceful rays":

> In vain the sight dejected to the ground
> Stoops for relief; thence *hot ascending steams*
> And *keen reflection pain*.[18]

As the poet retires to the "sweetness of the shade," "bold fancy" sends him on a "daring flight" to the torrid zone, where the excesses of heat and light are constant, where "with ardent blaze" the sun "looks *gaily fierce* o'er all the dazzling air."[19] Here he feels the excess of light, in which sublimity—combined of majesty and terror—is found:

> The parent sun himself
> Seems o'er this world of slaves to tyrannize,
> And, with oppressive ray the *roseate bloom*
> *Of beauty blasting*, gives the gloomy hue
> And feature gross.[20]

---

[17] Ibid., ll. 861-862. This distinction is common among the poets; the "awful" God creates whirlwinds, volcanoes, tempests, earthquakes; the "smiling" God is responsible for the loveliness, charm, delicacy of external nature.

[18] "Summer," ll. 437-439. The italics in these passages are, of course, mine.

[19] Ibid., ll. 637-638.   [20] Ibid., ll. 884-888.

In these regions the poet finds none of the tender, kind, placid, charming emotions which he had discovered in "Spring" :

> Love dwells not there,
> The *soft regards*, the *tenderness* of life,
> The heart-shed tear, the *ineffable delight*
> Of sweet humanity. . . .
> The very brute creation there
> *This rage partakes,* and *burns with horrid fire.*[21]

This is a region of "the rage intense Of brazen-vaulted skies," of thunderstorms, of the lurid blaze of volcanoes, of earthquakes; here Nature suffers in excess. This is also a region of perpetual light, more severe, more extreme than even the light of midsummer in the British Isles. There is majesty in the light of these regions—but there is also danger. Even when we return with Thomson to the British Isles, we are conscious still of the excesses of nature, of summer thunderstorms with flashing lightning, of light too strong for man to bear. "Beauty" appears in "Summer" only at those times of day when the full force of light is abated: the early morning; calm following a summer storm; evening when "the Sun has lost his rage," and, heat and light assuaged, the time comes for the poet to walk abroad among the delightful hills of England. Upon one occasion in "Summer," Thomson compares the "beauty" of familiar and quiet light with the former "sublimity," when after a summer storm, "from the face of Heaven the shattered clouds Tumultuous rove," and Nature "shines out afresh," while in the rainbow appears the yellow "glittering robe of joy"; here alone he says: " 'Tis beauty all."[22] Except for such occasional moments, "Summer" is a season of majesty and terror, so far as light is concerned; and, for the most part, color is conspicuous by its absence.

Occasionally—but only momentarily—in "Autumn" and

[21] Ibid., ll. 890-897.　　　　[22] Ibid., l. 1233.

"Winter" we feel the sublimity of light. Light is "infinite splendor! wide-investing all"[23]; "Earth's universal face . . . Is one wild dazzling waste"[24]; "The full ethereal round . . . Shines out intensely keen, and all one cope Of starry glitter"[25]; the earth in winter is a "glittering waste" of "unbounded wilds," when "snows swell on snows amazing to the sky."[26] Thomson's important distinction between the "beautiful" and "sublime," so far as light and color were concerned, occurred in "Spring" and "Summer." That the distinction was self-conscious and not merely fortuitous, and that it had been made even more clear to Thomson by the Newtonian discoveries, certain chronological facts would seem to indicate. Thomson was working upon "Summer" in 1726 or early 1727; before he published it, he interrupted his labors in order to write the memorial verses to Newton, which involved a careful study of the theories of the *Opticks* —whether in Newton's own words or those of his expositors Unlike the majority of his poetical predecessors (with the exception of Blackmore), Thomson really understood the implications of the *Opticks* in 1727. At the same time, Thomson was in close touch through correspondence with his Scottish friend, David Mallett, who was writing his *Excursion* as a complement to the earlier "Seasons."[27] "Sublimity," Thomson wrote to Mallett, "must be the character of your piece," and he suggested to his friend subjects and themes which might well be added to *The Excursion*. Mallett and Thomson interchanged their manuscripts, and as in "Summer," published in 1727 after the death of Newton, Thomson drew from Mallett, so Mallett in *The Excursion* drew from Thomson. "Sublimity" was the "character" of both their

[23] "Autumn," l. 1210.   [24] "Winter," ll. 238-239.
[25] Ibid., ll. 738-741.   [26] Ibid., l. 905.
[27] Cf. Peter Cunningham, "James Thomson and David Mallett," *Miscellanies of the Philobiblon Society*, IV, 1857-1858; McKillop, *Background of Thomson's Seasons*, pp. 70, 129; Samuel Monk, *The Sublime*, New York, 1935, pp. 89-90.

pieces. Indeed, Mallett's practice in his poem affords an interesting commentary upon Thomson's self-conscious development of the "sublime" in "Summer." Mallett, too, went back to Addison's categories in *Pleasures of the Imagination*:

> Thus roaming with adventurous wing the globe
> From scene to scene excursive, I behold
> In all her workings, *beauteous, great, or new,*
> Fair Nature, and in all with wonder trace
> The sovereign Maker.[28]

Mallett divided his attention equally between the terrestrial world and the cosmic universe, devoting one book to each; in that division Thomson's distinction between the beauty of color and the sublimity of light was implicit. While there is color in *The Excursion*, it is confined to the first book; there is—on an even more prodigal scale than in "Summer"—the sublimity of light, which, in the first book dealing with the terrestrial world, appears chiefly in connection with storms, volcanoes, and other dire manifestations of nature, and in the second book in connection with ethereal light, as the poet's imagination journeys to the stars, the planets, and the sun.

One other element in Thomson's "aesthetic" of light must be considered before we pass on to the further development of such an aesthetic in Akenside and Burke. If light may be sublime, so, too, may darkness and obscurity, consisting in the absence of light. The eighteenth century "school of night" felt sublimity not less but sometimes more than did the descriptive poets of day—as Young's *Night Thoughts* amply proves, for Young was a poet not of the beautiful, but of the sublime. In "the midnight depth" Thomson experienced "horror" as in the blaze of tropical sun:

> Deep-roused, I feel
> A sacred terror, a severe delight
> Creep through my mortal frame.[29]

[28] *The Excursion*; Chalmers, XIV. 21.   [29] "Summer," ll. 540-541.

As night blotted out day in "Autumn" the poet was aware of an emotional response to the "sublime" as the vast, the grand, the magnificent. He himself suggested the contrast between the "infinite splendour" of the light of day, and the magnificence and vastness of night, in which beauty is lost:

> Now black and deep the night begins to fall,
> A shade immense! Sunk in the quenching gloom,
> Magnificent and vast, are heaven and earth.
> Order confounded lies, *all beauty void,*
> Distinction lost, and gay variety
> One universal blot—such the fair power
> Of light to kindle and create the whole.[30]

The effect of darkness to various eighteenth century poets was often analogous to the effect of excessive light. Locke to the contrary notwithstanding, it, too, was a sense-impression: "So Darkness strikes the sense no less than Light,"[31] said Pope, expressing a truism of the period. Locke, in his *Essay*, had discussed both darkness and the effect of excessive light[32] and, moreover, had quoted a letter from Newton, in which the great scientist had commented upon his own experience in observing light which caused temporary blindness and almost cost him his sight.[33]

> Excessive beauty, like a flash of light,
> Seems more to weaken, than to please the sight,

wrote Walter Harte in his "Essay on Painting."[34] Aaron Hill made the same point more verbosely in speaking about the comparative effect of color and light upon man's sense:

> [God] veil'd each path
> To heaven's blue lawns, with clouds, that shift each hour,
> Form, texture, hue—to suit their painted glow

[30] "Autumn," ll. 1138-1144.
[31] Locke denied that it was a sense-impression; see below, p. 127.
[32] *Essay Concerning Human Understanding,* II, vii, 4.
[33] Newton's letter to Locke is mentioned in the *Essay,* I. 237; and quoted in a note, I. 237-238.
[34] "Essay on Painting"; Chalmers, XVI. 322.

To man's undazzled gaze—attemp'ring lights
That teach the sun's too fervid beam to break
In colouring rays, and touch the sight, *more safe*.[35]

II

IT WAS Akenside rather than Thomson who brought into a semiphilosophical system the theories of the "sublime" and "beautiful" in relation to light and color. Thomson was primarily a descriptive poet; interested in and responsive to philosophical theories though he was, he remained a poet of nature rather than of the mind of man. Akenside prided himself upon being a "philosophical" poet, an eclectic who drew from many systems of philosophy, and welded those systems into still another which he felt his own. He was abstract rather than concrete, as Thomson was concrete rather than abstract. In *The Pleasures of Imagination,* first published in 1744, he attempted to bring Addison's earlier categories up-to-date for the mid-eighteenth century:

> Know then, whate'er of nature's pregnant stores,
> Whate'er of mimic art's reflected forms
> With love and admiration thus inflame
> The pow'rs of fancy, her delighted sons
> To three illustrious orders have referr'd:
> Three sister-graces, whom the painter's hand,
> The poet's tongue confesses: the *sublime*,
> The *wonderful*, the *fair*.[36]

In one of his most familiar passages, Akenside classified the different types of imagination in accordance with their chief response to the "sublime" and "beautiful":

> Diff'rent minds
> Incline to different objects: one pursues
> The vast alone, the wonderful, the wild;

[35] "Free Thoughts upon Faith," in *Works of the Late Aaron Hill*, London, 1753, IV. 240.
[36] *Pleasures of Imagination*, I. 139-146. The italics in this case are Akenside's.

> Another sighs for harmony, and grace,
> And gentlest beauty.[37]

In his early version of *The Pleasures of Imagination*, Akenside equated color with beauty. While, in his invocation
to Beauty, the poet hailed her as "Brightest progeny of
heav'n," it is clear that response to beauty was a simpler matter than response to sublimity. The idea of "order" was
fundamental to Akenside: with somewhat different meaning,
he might have said with Sir Thomas Browne: "All things
began in order; so shall they end, according to the ordainer
of order."[38] It is not Reason, but the lesser faculty, "indulgent
Fancy" (a term which Akenside, unlike Addison, frequently
distinguished from "Imagination"), which delights in color;
she finds pleasure less, as Reason, in "majestic Truth" than in

> Fiction . . . upon her vagrant wings
> Wafting ten thousand colours thro' the air,
> And, by the glances of her magic eye,
> Combining each in endless, fairy forms,
> Her wild creation.[39]

In a long passage (a combination of Addison, Shaftesbury,
and various Neoplatonic predecessors) in which Akenside
attempted "to trace the rising lustre" of Nature's charms
"thro' various being's fair proportion'd scale," from their
"first twilight" to "meridian splendour," the beauty of simple
color found the lowest place in the "scale":

> Of degree
> The least and lowliest, in th'effusive warmth
> Of colours mingling with a random blaze,
> Doth beauty dwell. Then higher in the line
> And variation of determin'd shape,

[37] *Ibid.*, III. 546-550.
[38] The most recent interpretation of Akenside may be found in Alfred
O. Aldridge's article, "The Eclecticism of Mark Akenside's 'The Pleasures of Imagination,'" *Journal of the History of Ideas*, V. 292-314.
[39] *Pleasures of Imagination*, I. 14-18.

> Where truth's eternal measures mark the bound
> Of circle, cube, or sphere. The third ascent
> Unites this varied symmetry of parts
> With colour's bland allurement. . . .
> But more lovely still
> Is nature's charm, where to the full consent
> Of complicated members, to the bloom
> Of colour, and the vital change of growth,
> Life's holy flame and piercing sense are giv'n,
> And active motion speaks the temper'd soul.[40]

The untutored peasant, watching the sunset, might be as responsive to the simple beauty of color as the man of learning who understands the nature of things:

> Ask the swain
> Who journeys homeward from a summer day's
> Long labour, why, forgetful of his toils,
> And due repose, he loiters to behold
> The sunshine gleaming as thro' amber clouds,
> O'er all the western sky; full soon, I ween,
> His rude expression and untutor'd airs,
> Beyond the pow'r of language, will unfold
> The form of beauty smiling at his heart.[41]

In the various "excursions," in which Akenside's imagination ranged over the world and through the cosmic universe seeking the sources of the "sublime, the wonderful, the fair," and in the many "visions" through which he pointed the morals that adorned his tale, we find the constant association of color with beauty. In his invocation to Beauty, he said:

> How shall I trace thy features? where select
> The roseate hues to emulate thy bloom?
> Haste then, my song, thro' nature's wide expanse,
> Haste, then, and gather all her comeliest wealth,
> Whate'er bright spoils the florid earth contains,

[40] *Ibid.*, I. 442-480.   [41] *Ibid.*, III. 526-534.

Whate'er the waters, or the liquid air,
To deck thy lovely labour.[42]

Flying with "laughing Autumn to th' Atlantic isles," he saw that

where'er his fingers touch the fruitful grove,
The branches shoot with gold; where'er his step
Marks the glad soil, the tender clusters glow
With purple ripeness, and invest each hill
As with the blushes of an evening sky.[43]

So far, however, Akenside has suggested little more than the conventional and orthodox association of color with beauty. In at least one instance he departed from mere convention, attempting to determine how color may ascend from the "beautiful" to the "sublime." While color is ordinarily charming, delightful, beautiful, yet, carried to excess, involved with vastness or extraordinary emotion—particularly with the sublimity of light—it may momentarily become sublime:

when to raise the meditated scene,
The flame of passion, thro' the struggling soul
Deep-kindled, shows across that sudden blaze
The object of its rapture, vast of size,
With fiercer colours and a night of shade.[44]

In this passage we approach Akenside's theory of the sublimity of light. To be sure, there are moments in *The Pleasures of Imagination*, when Akenside merely followed the Scriptural, Pythagorean and Miltonic fashion of referring "sublime" light to the "Author of Sublimity":

whence the robes of light,
Which thus invest her with more lovely pomp
Than fancy can describe? Whence but from thee,
O source divine of ever-flowing love,
And thy unmeasur'd goodness?[45]

[42] *Ibid.*, I. 281-287.   [43] *Ibid.*, I. 290-294.
[44] *Ibid.*, II. 136-140.   [45] *Ibid.*, III. 485-489.

While beauty and color, in their simpler manifestations, might be associated with Fiction and appeal to "indulgent Fancy," "majestic Truth" dwelt in sublime light:

> shall I mention, where coelestial truth
> Her awful light discloses, to effuse
> A more majestic pomp on beauty's frame?[46]

For true sublimity, light must be either excessive, sudden, painful to the observer, associated with vastness, or in marked contrast to darkness. One of Akenside's "visions" of sublimity occurred "in the windings of an ancient wood" at evening on an autumn day, when "the shade More horrid nodded o'er me," and "dark As midnight storms"

> the scene of human things
> Appear'd before me; desarts, burning sands,
> Where the parch'd adder dies; the frozen north
> And desolation blasting all the west
> With rapine and with murder: tyrant-pow'r
> Here sits inthron'd in blood; the baleful charms
> Of superstition there infect the skies,
> And turn the sun to horror.[47]

Across this fearful scene, combining, in characteristic eighteenth century style both "horrid" dark and "horror," came sudden light:

> A flashing torrent of coelestial day
> Burst thro' the shadowy void. With slow descent
> A purple cloud came floating thro' the sky,
> And pois'd at length within the circling trees,
> Hung obvious to my view; till opening wide
> Its lucid orb, a more than human form
> Emerging lean'd majestic o'er my head,
> And instant thunder shook the conscious grove.
> Then melted into air the liquid cloud,
> And all the shining vision stood revealed.[48]

[46] *Ibid.*, II. 97-99.   [47] *Ibid.*, II. 205-212.   [48] *Ibid.*, II. 221-230.

In another "vision," the beauty and the sublimity of light are contrasted, as two ethereal visitants appeared to the poet. One was the essence of beauty, involving both color and light:

> Eternal youth
> O'er all her form its glowing honours breath'd;
> And smiles eternal, from her candid eyes,
> Flow'd like the dewy lustre of the morn
> Effusive trembling on the placid waves.
> The spring of heav'n had shed its blushing spoils
> To bind her sable tresses: full diffus'd
> Her yellow mantle floated in the breeze.[49]

The other visitant was symbolic not of the beautiful, but of the sublime:

> More sublime
> The heav'nly partner mov'd. The prime of age
> Composed her steps. The presence of a god
> High on the circle of her brow inthron'd,
> From each majestic motion darted awe, . . .
> A matron's robe,
> White as the sunshine streams thro' vernal clouds,
> Her stately form invested.[50]

As "the immortal pair forsook th' enamell'd green," and rising above the atmosphere ascended into ether, Akenside brought together his various theories of the sublimity of light:

> Rays of limpid light
> Gleam'd round their path; coelestial sounds were heard,
> And thro' the fragrant air aethereal dews
> Distill'd around them; till at once the clouds
> Disparting wide in midway sky, withdrew
> Their airy veil, and left a bright expanse
> Of empyrean flame, where spent and drown'd,
> Afflicted vision plung'd in vain to scan
> What object it involv'd. My feeble eyes
> Indur'd not.[51]

[49] Ibid., II. 409-416.   [50] Ibid., II. 420-433.   [51] Ibid., II. 435-444.

III

IN *The Pleasures of Imagination* Akenside, the eclectic, taking his point of departure from Addison, had gathered together theories of the "sublime" and "beautiful," which had been emerging in the first half of the eighteenth century. He prided himself upon being a "philosophical" poet; while he was no true philosopher, he went far in his attempt at not only a systematization of the theories of his time, but a versified illustration of them. To what extent *The Pleasures of Imagination* served as the specific point of departure for the philosophical work in which these tendencies of the time were finally reduced to order and method remains a matter of surmise. Yet in seeking the ancestry of Burke's *Philosophical Enquiry into the Origin of Our Ideas of the Sublime and Beautiful,* it is well to remember that eighteenth century philosophers read poetry and popular essays, as essayists and poets read philosophy. Burke's essay was not published until 1756 or 1757,[52] but there is little reason to doubt the statement that its original draft was written about 1748, when Burke was not more than nineteen, and was read before the club he had founded at Trinity College, Dublin. Addison's *Pleasures of the Imagination* had been "classic" for many years; Thomson's *Seasons,* in various editions, particularly in the revision of 1744, was immensely popular, and Akenside's *Pleasures of Imagination* was rapidly becoming one of the most widely read poems of the period. Upon such meat had this our young Caesar fed that he was to grow so great![53]

---

[52] The date commonly given for the *Enquiry* is 1756, but there is good reason for dating it 1757; see F. A. Pottle, *Notes and Queries,* CXLVIII (1925), p. 80; Helen Drew, *Modern Language Notes,* I (1935), pp. 29-31.

[53] I am not, of course, suggesting that the various critical and philosophical works treating the sublime and beautiful were not influential; discussion of them may be found conveniently brought together in Samuel Monk, *The Sublime,* particularly in Chapters III and IV. It merely seems to me that Akenside's poem might well have served as a point of departure for the young student at Trinity College.

Similarities between Burke's *Enquiry* and Addison's essays clearly exist and have always been recognized. Not only did Burke pick up many of Addison's points in the *Pleasures*, agreeing and disagreeing, but in later editions, he, too, prefaced his discussion of the imagination, as had Addison, with a disquisition upon "Taste," in which he took exception to the earlier essayist's theory that Taste was a "faculty" of the soul. Whatever Burke's actual debt to Thomson and Akenside, he showed in his treatment of color and light many similarities with the theories of the latter and the practice of the former.

In his treatment of color in relationship to beauty, Burke said little that was not entirely conventional. He listed as "qualities of beauty, as they are merely sensible qualities," smallness, smoothness, gradual variation, delicacy, and color, and discussed in some detail the kinds of color which make for beauty:

> As to the colours usually found in beautiful bodies, it may be somewhat difficult to ascertain them, because in the several parts of nature, there is an infinite variety. However even in this variety we may mark out something on which to settle. First, the colours of beautiful bodies must not be dusky or muddy, but clean and fair. Secondly, they must not be of the strongest kind. Those which seem most appropriate to beauty are the milder of every sort; light greens; soft blues; weak whites; pink reds, and violets. Thirdly, if the colours be strong and vivid, they are always diversified, and the object is never of one strong colour; there are almost always such a number of them (as in variegated flowers), that the strength and glare of each is considerably abated.[54]

Later in considering the effect of the qualities of beauty he had already discussed, he returned to his statement that "the colours of beautiful bodies must not be dusky or muddy, but

[54] *A Philosophical Enquiry into the Origin of Our Ideas of the Sublime and Beautiful*, Philadelphia, 1806, Part III, Section XVII.

clean and fair," explaining "the agreeable effects" upon principles of optics:

> Suppose I look at a bottle of muddy liquor, of a blue or red colour: the blue or red rays cannot pass clearly to the eye, but are suddenly and unequally stopped by the intervention of little opaque bodies, which, without preparation, change the idea, and change it, too, into one disagreeable in its own nature. . . . But when the ray passes without such opposition through the glass or liquor, when the glass or liquor is quite transparent, the light is something softened in the passage, which makes it more agreeable even as light; and the liquor reflecting all the rays of its proper colour evenly, it has such an effect on the eye as smooth opaque bodies have on the eye and the touch; so that the pleasure here is compounded of the softness of the transmitted, and the evenness of the reflected light.[55]

Ordinarily, color belongs to the realm of beauty, but it may produce an effect of sublimity if it is strong and violent on the one hand or sad and melancholy on the other:

> Among colours, such as are soft and cheerful (except, perhaps, a strong red which is cheerful) are unfit to produce grand images. An immense mountain, covered with a shining green turf, is nothing, in this respect, to one dark and gloomy; the cloudy sky is more grand than the blue, and night more sublime and solemn than day. Therefore in historical painting, a gay or gaudy drapery can never have a happy effect: and in buildings, when the highest degree of the sublime is intended, the materials and ornaments ought neither to be white, nor green, nor yellow, nor blue, nor of a pale red, nor violet, nor spotted, but of sad and fuscous colours, as black, or brown, or deep purple, and the like.[56]

Burke's sections upon light are more interesting and significant than those on color. "Mere light" is too common and ordinary to be associated aesthetically with either beauty or

[55] *Ibid.*, Part IV, Section XXVI.   [56] *Ibid.*, Part II, Section XVII.

sublimity, though we have seen that the clarity of light might contribute to beauty:

> With regard to light, to make it a cause capable of producing the sublime, it must be attended with some circumstances besides its bare faculty of showing other objects. Mere light is too common a thing to make a strong impression on the mind; and without a strong impression nothing can be sublime. But such a light as that of the sun, immediately exerted on the eye, as it overpowers the sense, is a very great idea. Light of an inferior strength to this, if it moves with great celerity, has the same power; for lightning is certainly productive of grandeur, which it owes chiefly to the extreme velocity of its motion. A quick transition from light to darkness, or from darkness to light, has yet a greater effect. But darkness is more productive of sublime ideas than light. . . . Extreme light, by overcoming the organs of sight, obliterates all objects, so as in its effect exactly to resemble darkness. After looking for some time at the sun, two black spots, the impression which it leaves, seem to dance before our eyes. Thus are two ideas, as opposite as can be imagined, reconciled in the extremes of both; and both, in spite of their opposite nature, brought to concur in producing the sublime.[57]

Among the qualities of the sublime, Burke listed astonishment, terror, obscurity, power, vastness, and magnificence. The sublimity of light partakes in some degree of each of them: light may astonish by its suddenness, overwhelm the human eye by its vastness and power, evoke an aesthetic response by its magnificence, or rouse the passions either by its terror in excess or by its "privation." Burke showed himself of the post-Newtonian generation in the many passages in which he paused to analyze the effects of the sublime in connection with the processes of sight, as for example in his discussion "Why visual objects of great dimension are sublime":

[57] *Ibid.*, Part II, Section XV. The omitted passage is a tribute to the sublimity of Milton's handling of light and darkness, in connection with Deity.

Vision is performed by having a picture formed by the rays of light which are reflected from the object painted in one piece, instantaneously, on the retina, or last nervous part of the eye. Or, according to others, there is but one point of any object painted on the eye in such a manner as to be perceived at once; but, by moving the eye, we gather up with great celerity the several parts of the object, so as to form one uniform piece. If the former opinion be allowed, it will be considered, that, though all the light reflected from a large body should strike the eye in one instant, yet we must suppose that the body itself is formed of a vast number of distinct points, every one of which, or the ray from every one, makes an impression on the retina. So that, though the image of one point should cause but a small tension of this membrane, another, and another, and another stroke, must in their progress cause a very great one, until it arrives at last to the highest degree; and the whole capacity of the eye, vibrating in all its parts, must approach near to the nature of what causes pain, and consequently must produce an idea of the sublime.[58]

"All *general* privations are great," Burke declared, "because they are all terrible: *Vacuity, Darkness, Solitude*, and *Silence*."[59] While light may involve sublimity because of either magnificence or "horror," the "privation" of light is even more a cause of terror. Darkness, Burke said, is more productive of sublime ideas than light; light, too excessive for human sight, inevitably becomes darkness. The sublimity of darkness might, on the one hand, rise from pain, as in excessive light; on the other hand, it might arise from terror. Here, in his attempt to develop his own most characteristic thesis, Burke departed from Locke:

It is Mr. Locke's opinion, that darkness is not naturally an idea of terror; and that, though an excessive light is painful to the sense, that the greatest excess of darkness is in no way troublesome. . . . The authority of this great man is doubtless as great as that of any man can be, and it seems to stand in the

<hr />

[58] *Ibid.*, Part IV, Section IX.   [59] *Ibid.,* Part II, Section VII.

way of our general principle. We have considered darkness as a cause of the sublime; and we have all along considered the sublime as depending on some modification of pain or terror; so that, if darkness be in no way painful or terrible . . . it can be no source of the sublime.[60]

The long, carefully reasoned sections which follow are most interesting in showing the extent to which the generation which followed Locke and Newton found it necessary to enter into close analysis of the physiological processes of sight in order to explain its psychological effects. Here Burke added still another character to the procession of the blind: a boy born blind who gained sight at the age of thirteen or fourteen, and who, immediately upon seeing a black object, displayed great uneasiness—a circumstance which served to aid Burke in his insistence that the fear of darkness is not merely the result of childhood association, engendered by nurses' tales of ghosts and goblins. Burke analyzed in detail various theories of the physiological effects of darkness, entering into a lengthy discussion of its effects upon the human eye, insisting that there are such effects, and that "any one will find, if he opens his eyes, and makes an effort to see in a dark place, that a very perceptible pain ensues." The passage —with the accompanying discussion of the difference between "darkness" and "blackness"—serves as an excellent summary of various attitudes toward darkness, in contrast with light, which we have seen in some of the poets, and with which we are well acquainted in other "melancholy," "midnight," and "graveyard" writers. While Burke discussed the association of darkness with superstition and legend, which may be peculiar to an individual and the result of early experience, he was convinced that the terror of darkness is not an individual but a universal instinct. This was in part because of its potential danger:

[60] *Ibid.*, Part IV, Section XIV.

. . . for, in utter darkness, it is impossible to know in what degree of safety we stand; we are ignorant of the objects that surround us; we may every moment strike against some dangerous obstruction; we may fall down a precipice the first step we take; and, if an enemy approach, we know not in what quarter to defend ourselves; in such a case strength is no sure protection; wisdom can only act by guess; the boldest are staggered; and he who would pray for nothing else towards his defence, is forced to pray for light.[61]

Even apart from danger, darkness remained to Burke an object of uneasiness. Blackness, which "is but a partial darkness" has in it—as to Burke's blind boy—something painful to the sight, even though custom may reconcile us to it, so that the terror abates with familiarity. Yet "black will always have something melancholy in it, because the sensory will always find the change to it, from other colours, too violent; or, if it occupy the whole compass of the sight, it will then be darkness; and what was said of darkness, will be applicable here."[62] Characteristic product of the "Age of Reason" as he was, Burke's objectivity and dispassionateness, his analytical mind, his literal style, striving for exactness rather than for beauty, were far removed from mysticism or mystery. But in his prolonged discussion of darkness, and in his insistence that the terror of darkness is not peculiar to an individual but is "an association of a more general nature, an association which takes in all mankind," we feel a momentary stirring of some instinct deep-planted in humanity, a universal terror of the human race. The unreasoning fear of the child "afraid of the dark," the superstitious dread of the savage, was in kind if not degree the response of even the "philosophic mind" in the Age of Enlightenment, attempting to dispel by the cool light of reason the terrors of darkness which oppressed man. Light might be sublime, because magnificent, painful, or dangerous; darkness, even more than the other "general pri-

[61] *Ibid.*   [62] *Ibid.*, Part IV, Section XVIII.

vations" was still more sublime, because still more terrible.
One kind of sublimity was experienced and expressed by the
great poet "blinded by excess of light" who closed his eyes in
endless night; another was that of Akenside's vision, beginning with the magnificence of light, ending with its pain,
when "afflicted vision plung'd in vain to scan What object it
involv'd. My feeble eyes endured not." Thomson felt both
the grandeur and terror of the deprivation of light; at one
moment he experienced "a sacred terror, a severe delight," at
another he felt the "privation" of night, with its obliteration
of all that man calls beautiful:

> Order confounded lies, all beauty void,
> Distinction lost, and gay variety
> One universal blot. . . .[63]

And yet it was not Burke nor Akenside nor Thomson who
gave the finest expression to the deep-seated eighteenth century response to that great "privation." It was Pope, who at
the end of *The Dunciad* expressed in truly "sublime" style
both the majesty and the terror of universal darkness:

> In vain, in vain—the all-composing Hour
> Resistless falls: the Muse obeys the Pow'r.
> She comes! she comes! the sable Throne behold
> Of Night primaeval and of Chaos old.
> Before her, Fancy's gilded clouds decay,
> And all its varying Rain-bows die away.
> Wit shoots in vain its momentary fires,
> The meteor drops, and in a flash expires. . . .
> Thus at her felt approach and secret might,
> Art after Art goes out, and all is Night.
> See skulking Truth to her old cavern fled,
> Mountains of Casuistry heaped o'er her head!
> Philosophy, that lean'd on Heav'n before,
> Shrinks to her second cause, and is no more.
> Physic of Metaphysic begs defence,

[63] "Autumn," ll. 1141-1143.

And Metaphysic calls for aid on Sense!
See Mystery to Mathematics fly!
In vain! they gaze, turn giddy, rave, and die. . . .
Lo! thy dread Empire, CHAOS! is restor'd;
Light dies before thy uncreating word;
Thy hand, great Anarch! lets the curtain fall,
And universal Darkness buries All.

The rest should be silence; as Pope said the last word on the sublimity of darkness, so, for many poets of his time, he said the last word on "Physic" and "Metaphysic." There could be no better transition from the "aesthetics" to the "metaphysics" which poets read into the *Opticks*.

CHAPTER SIX

METAPHYSICAL IMPLICATIONS OF THE OPTICKS

I HAVE ONLY BEGUN THE ANALYSIS OF WHAT REMAINS TO BE DISCOVER'D ABOUT LIGHT AND ITS EFFECTS UPON THE FRAME OF NATURE, HINTING SEVERAL THINGS ABOUT IT, AND LEAVING THE HINTS TO BE EXAMIN'D AND IMPROV'D BY THE FARTHER EXPERIMENTS AND OBSERVATIONS OF SUCH AS ARE INQUISITIVE.[1]

S O FAR we have seen the poets unanimous in their admiration for the great Newton. They have accepted without question the prismatic discovery of colors. They have proved themselves willing to study the Newtonian physics, to versify Newton's theories, sometimes to transmute them into poetry. They have been greatly interested in problems of the nature of sight, sympathizing with the blind men of Molyneux, Locke, Steele, because to the sightless the external world remains unknown or only partially conceived: "Without thee Nature lies unmeaning gloom." These were not lazy poets, content to take easy ways out of intellectual dilemmas, "responding" or "reacting" without attempting to understand their responses and reactions. The Romanticists to the contrary notwithstanding, they felt, though they also tried to think clearly. Products of the Age of Reason, they believed that God had given man reason in order that he might look through nature up to nature's God.

From now on, however, they will begin to part company, sometimes from philosophers and scientists, sometimes from each other. Poets, after all, are poets; even the most scien-

1 *Opticks*, Book III, Part I, Query 31; *ed. cit.*, p. 405.

tific versifiers are not scientists, the most philosophical poets not philosophers. Poets, philosophers, scientists may visit each other's countries of the mind with pleasure and profit, sometimes bringing home bags of gold. But as Reynolds said: "*Poeta nascitur* . . . I never thought my self naturaliz'd." Occasionally a man may find himself temporarily at home in a country of his adoption: Plato, for all his strictures on poets, entered into their country, yet remained a philosopher; Lucretius was at home in both realms—and where is he finally to be entombed? Bruno perhaps came nearer than any other to living in two worlds at once; since he guessed right, he has become a philosopher; had he guessed wrong, he would still be a poet. Dante and Milton passed over from the other side, yet there is no question which country they claimed, and which claims them. Many of the eighteenth century poets overstepped the boundaries too often for their own good; as a result they are likely to be refused by both countries, to end as expatriates or even as men without a country. Yet among them were some who, having temporarily forgotten their poetic heritage in their desire for foreign travel, became aware of it when faced with the ultimate implications which the Age of Newton read into the master.

I

To some extent even Newton—though he seemed to dwell in his own rarefied "Aether"—became associated with the increasing distrust of science on the part of one group who feared the extremes to which the scientific approach to "truth" was tending. Akenside, for all his admiration, warned:

> There, Science! veil thy daring eye,
> Nor dive too deep, nor soar too high.[2]

Pope in the *Essay on Man* went further in criticizing tendencies of his generation:

[2] Akenside, "Hymn to Science."

Go, wond'rous creature! mount where Science guides,
Go, measure earth, weigh air, and state the tides;
Instruct the planets in what orbs to run,
Correct old Time, and regulate the Sun; . . .
Go, teach Eternal Wisdom how to rule—
Then drop into thyself, and be a fool![3]

Pope's attitude in the *Essay on Man* was not only consistent with the attitude of the earlier Scriblerians toward the excesses of science and philosophy at all times, but indicated a specific irritation at the extremes of adulation to which the Newtonians were going in the years immediately following the death of their idol, when they had so adored him that Newton bade fair to ascend to the throne of Deity, displacing God Himself. It was not Newton, but the Newtonians, whom Pope castigated:

Superior beings, when of late they saw
A mortal Man unfold all Nature's law,
Admired such Wisdom in an earthly shape,
And shew'd a Newton, as we shew an Ape.[4]

Newton had discovered the fundamental law of the heavens; he seemed to have answered Job's question: "Canst thou bind the sweet influences of the Pleiades?" Yet not even Newton, who discovered the laws of gravity and light, could solve human problems much more important to those who believed that the "proper study of mankind is man," and that

Thro' worlds unnumbered though the God be known,
'Tis ours to trace him only in our own.[5]

[3] *Essay on Man*, II. 19-30.
[4] *Ibid.*, II. 31-34. The respectful treatment which Pope—in common with his age—accorded Newton was probably not only the result of the fact that even those who opposed the extremes of science recognized Newton's own pre-eminence, but also a tribute to Newton's own humility; the generation knew that Newton had never set himself up as an oracle, that he would have resented the adulation his memory received, that he felt himself only a child gathering pebbles upon the seashore of knowledge.
[5] *Ibid.*, I. 21-22.

After all, Newton, who had learned so much about the universe, understood the eternal mysteries no better than did the rudest swain:

> Could he, whose rules the rapid Comet bind,
> Describe or fix one movement of his Mind?
> Who saw its fires here rise, and there descend,
> Explain his own beginning, or his end?
> Alas, what wonder![6]

"Happy is he who knows the causes of things"—but is he? Not necessarily, according to the school of Pope, more concerned with ethics than with metaphysics. There is a limit beyond which science and metaphysics cannot go—this was a persistent warning of one group of the eighteenth century, who opposed the current excitement of discovery, the Baconian belief that man could discover all the secrets of Nature and command her. There are limitations to science; there are limitations to Reason; a chief difficulty lies in human nature:

> Man's superior part,
> Uncheck'd may rise, and climb from art to art:
> But when his own great work is but begun,
> What Reason weaves, by Passion is undone.
> Trace Science then, with Modesty thy guide;
> First strip off all her equipage of Pride;
> Deduct what is but Vanity or Dress,
> Or Learning's Luxury, or Idleness;
> Or tricks to shew the stretch of human brain,
> Mere curious pleasures, or ingenious pain;
> Expunge the whole, or lop th' excrescent parts
> Of all our Vices have created Arts;
> Then see how little the remaining sum,
> Which serv'd the past, and must the times to come.[7]

The extreme position of the Newtonians, opposed by Pope and his group, may be seen in the most important memorial-poem, published in 1728 by Newton's friend, J. T. Desagu-

[6] *Ibid.*, II. 35-39.   [7] *Ibid.*, II. 39-52.

liers, who was not only a scientist in his own right, but an important liaison-officer between technical scientists and laymen. In his *Newtonian System of the World, the Best Model of Government*,[8] Desaguliers read the Newtonian theories over into politics, insisting that the discoveries of the *Principia* should be applied to human thinking in all fields. There was no praise too lavish for Desaguliers; Newton had discovered all truth, had reformed all thinking; he had revealed the ways of God to man:

> Newton the unparallel'd, whose Name
> No Time will wear out of the Book of Fame,
> Coelestiall Science has promoted more,
> Than all the Sages that have shone before.
> Nature compell'd his piercing Mind obeys,
> And gladly shows him all her secret Ways;
> 'Gainst Mathematics she has no Defence,
> And yields t' experimental Consequence;
> His Tow'ring Genius, from its certain Cause
> Ev'ry Appearance *a priori* draws,
> And shews th' Almighty Architect's unalter'd Laws.[9]

Desaguliers was only one of many who seemed to feel that the Revelation according to Newton was greater than that according to Moses or St. John the Divine. It was to such lavish and unrestrained adulation that Pope replied in *The Dunciad*—to some extent in *The Dunciad* of 1728, written while the memorial-tributes to Newton were pouring forth

---

[8] *The Newtonian System of the World, the Best Model of Government, An Allegorical Poem*, Westminster, 1729. This was unquestionably the most important poem written at the time of Newton's death. Desaguliers' application of the theory of gravitation to political philosophy (in which Pope himself joined in the *Essay on Man*) persisted throughout the century, and is clearly seen as late as in Tom Paine. I have not discussed this work elsewhere, in spite of its significance, since Desaguliers was primarily concerned with the *Principia*, not with the *Opticks*.

[9] *The Newtonian System of the World*, p. 21.

from the presses—even more in the "New" or "Greater Dunciad" of 1741-42.[10]

Between the period of the early *Dunciad* and the "New Dunciad," the tide was turning. The high period of enthusiasm, following the death of Newton, was giving way to more reasoned and less exaggerated interpretations of his work. The tide was turning, too, so far as Locke was concerned; for while this period marked the flood tide of both Newton and Locke, the moment of high tide is the beginning of the ebb. The *Essay Concerning Human Understanding* was opposed in many "essays on the limitations of the human understanding." While Hume's *Essay on Human Nature*, written in 1734 and published in 1739, did not attract the wide public of his later works, its appearance at this particular time was significant, since Hume taught that the limits of human knowledge are the limits of sense-experience. So far as poetry was concerned, Pope's prestige, after the publication of the *Essay on Man*, was so great that his imitators vied with each other in developing the implications of his attacks upon science and philosophy. We may see a minor instance in Henry Jones, who has already entered these pages in a tribute to the "ladies" who studied Newton's theories of light and colors with "Mr. Booth" of Dublin. When the enthusiasm of the age was for science, Henry Jones offered it science; when the great Pope suggested the limitations of science and philosophy, Henry Jones wrote "An Essay on the Weakness of Human Knowledge," including in his criticism of Locke, Newton, whom he had hitherto praised:

> Our prying Eyes would pierce all Nature's store,
> Unlock her Secrets, turn her Treasures o'er;

[10] In my later quotations from *The Dunciad*, I have not attempted to discriminate among the various versions, but have considered the work as it was published in the complete version, when time had permitted Pope to "digest" the implications of the Newtonians, which were implied in passing in the early *Dunciad* and more fully developed in the *Essay on Man*.

Yet far within she shows the searching Ray;
Her mighty Master keeps the Mystick Key;
A nearer View's deny'd to mortal Sight;
Newton's transcendent Day must bound in Night.[11]

Henry Jones was, however, too insignificant a versifier and too much a trimmer to be considered seriously. A better example of the current attitude of minor poets of the school of Pope was Walter Harte's "Essay on Reason," in which Pope himself was said to have had a hand.[12] In the poem may be seen both the height of the popularity of Locke and Newton, and the reaction against implications which had been read into them. Its lesson is the classical doctrine of moderation, limitation, *nothing in excess*. Reason is important, yet there are limits to reason; science is a legitimate road to truth, but science has its limits; philosophy has discovered much, but it has not solved the perennial problems of man. The extent to which Locke and Newton had come to be combined in the minds of minor poets was shown in Harte's Lockean account of "the thinking faculty, its source, its pow'rs":

How stretch'd like Kneller's canvas first it lies,
Ere the soft tints awake, or outlines rise;
How till the finishing of thrice sev'n years,
The master figure Reason scarce appears: . . .
Yet in this infant state, by stealth, by chance,
The increasing mind still feels a slow advance,
Thro' the dark void ev'n gleams of truth can shoot,
And love of liberty upheaves at root. . . .
Sensation first, the ground-work of the whole,
Deals ray by ray each image to the soul;

[11] *Poems on Several Occasions*, London, 1749, pp. 64-65.
[12] The "Essay on Reason" was published in 1735; it may be found in Chalmers, XVI. 352-357. Chalmers says in his biographical sketch, p. 312, that Pope contributed to it "very considerably, although no part of his share can be determined except the first two lines":

From Truth's vast length, eternal and unknown,
Essence of God, coeval Reason shone.

[138]

Perception true to every nerve, receives
The various impulse, now exults, now grieves.
Thought works and ends, and dares afresh begin;
So whirlpools pour out streams, and suck them in;
That thought romantic Memory detains
In unknown cells, and in aerial chains;
Imagination thence her flow'rs translates;
And Fancy, emulous of God, creates:
Experience slowly moving next appears,
Wise but by habit, judging but by years,
Till Knowledge comes, a wise and gen'rous heir,
And opes the reservoir, averse to spare;
And Reason rises, the Newtonian Sun,
Moves all, guides all, and all sustains in one.[13]

In spite of his gift of Reason, man remains the "middle link in being's endless chain" who must not aspire to the angelic orders, must not envy the "microscopic eye" of the fly:

Then dare be wise, into thyself descend,
Sage to some purpose, studious to some end;
Search thine own heart, the well where knowledge lies;
Thence (not from higher earth) we catch the skies:
Leave myst'ry to the seraph's purer thought
Which takes in truth, as forms by streams are caught;
Leave lust to brutes, whose unhurt sense is such,
That tenfold transport thrills at ev'ry touch:
Holding the middle sphere where reason lies,
Than these more temp'rate, as than those more wise.[14]

This is the "knowledge within bounds" about which Milton's Angel cautioned Milton's Adam; it is the Christian humility, the classical doctrine of the *via media*, the golden mean. Reason in excess, like science carried beyond its legitimate limits, may be as dangerous as ignorance:

Reason, like virtue, in a medium lies:
A hair's-breadth more might make us mad, not wise,

[13] "Essay on Reason"; Chalmers, XVI. 354.
[14] Ibid., p. 354.

Out-know ev'n knowledge, and out-polish art,
Till Newton drops down giddy—a Descartes![15]

But there is no reason to invoke demigods when Zeus
himself is present. Pope said all that was to be said on this
side of the question in *The Dunciad*. Toward the end of the
third book, when his hero-villain looked into the future, Pope
suggested that if intellectual England continued as it bade
fair to do, the sons of "Dullness" (we should remember his
interpretation of this word, which implied not that his contemporaries knew too little, but that they prided themselves
on knowing too much) would preside over all Arts and
Sciences, and, self-conscious of their powers in discovering
the secrets of nature and the mysteries of Deity, would come
to worship man rather than God:

" 'Tis yours a Bacon or a Locke to blame,
A Newton's genius, or a Milton's flame:
But oh! with One, immortal One dispense;
The source of Newton's Light, of Bacon's Sense.
Content, each Emanation of his fires
That beams on earth, each Virtue he inspires,
Each Art he prompts, each Charm he can create,
Whate'er he gives, are giv'n for you to hate.
Persist, by all divine in Man unaw'd,
But, 'Learn, ye Dunces! not to scorn your God!' "[16]

For a moment, the earlier "Dunce," prophesying to the later
King of Dunces, had spoken seriously:

Thus he, for then a ray of Reason stole
Half through the solid darkness of his soul;
But soon the cloud returned—[17]

The theme of the "Greater Dunciad" indicates the extent to
which these attitudes had developed in the intervening years.
Pope himself said in his "Argument":

[15] Ibid., p. 353.   [16] *Dunciad*, III. 215-224.
[17] *Ibid.*, III. 225-227.

The Poet being in this Book, to declare the Completion of the Prophecies mentioned at the end of the former, makes a new Invocation: as the greater Poets are wont, when some high and worthy matter is to be sung. He shews the Goddess coming in her Majesty, to destroy Order and Science, and to substitute the Kingdom of the Dull upon earth.

The invocation, like the conclusion, of the fourth book dealt with light and darkness; as in many invocations of the period we remember both Milton and Newton:

> Yet, yet a moment, one dim Ray of Light
> Indulge, dread Chaos, and eternal Night!
> Of darkness visible so much be lent,
> As half to shew, half veil, the deep Intent.[18]

Here we find the "classical" position of the school of Pope—protest against the excesses to which the Age of Newton had gone in elevating science and metaphysics above religion and ethics, in believing that men had found ultimate "truth" in the books of mathematicians, scientists, philosophers:

> "What though we let some better sort of fool
> Thrid ev'ry science, run through ev'ry school?
> Never by tumbler through the hoops was shewn
> Such skill in passing all, and touching none;
> He may indeed (if sober all this time)
> Plague with Dispute, or persecute with Rhyme.
> We only furnish what he cannot use,
> Or wed to what he must divorce, a Muse:
> Full in the midst of Euclid dip at once,
> And petrify a Genius to a Dunce:
> Or set on Metaphysic ground to prance,
> Show all his paces, not a step advance. . . ."[19]

Of the making of many books there had been no end, and much study of those books seemed a weariness of the flesh to men who found the metaphysicians at best oversubtle in their spinning of "cobwebs of learning" out of their own sub-

[18] *Ibid.*, IV. 1-4.   [19] *Ibid.*, IV. 255-266.

stance, at worst absurd in clouding with elaborate philosophical jargon what was obvious to common sense:

> See! still thy own, the heavy Canon roll,
> And Metaphysic smokes involve the Pole.
> For thee we dim the eyes, and stuff the head
> With all such reading as was never read:
> For thee explain a thing till all men doubt it,
> And write about it, Goddess, and about it.
> So spins the silk-worm small its slender store,
> And labours till it clouds itself all o'er.[20]

Pope's answer to such "Newtonians" as Desaguliers, who attempted to claim all knowledge as the province of their master,
who found the road to truth in experimental science and in
philosophical theories rather than through faith and common
sense, was expressed in the words of the "Gloomy Clerk" in
one of the last sections in *The Dunciad*, a dialogue which
combines many of the themes which we have been considering:

> "O! would the Sons of Men once think their Eyes
> And Reason giv'n them but to study Flies!
> See Nature in some partial narrow shape,
> And let the Author of the Whole escape:
> Learn but to trifle; or, who most observe,
> To wonder at the Maker, not to serve!"
> "Be that my task" (replies a Gloomy Clerk,
> Sworn Foe to Myst'ry, yet divinely dark;
> Whose pious hope aspires to see the day
> When Moral Evidence shall quite decay,
> And damns implicit Faith, and holy lies,
> Prompt to impose and fond to dogmatize:)
> "Let others creep by timid steps, and slow,
> On plain Experience lay foundations low,
> By common sense to common knowledge bred,
> And last, to Nature's Cause through Nature led.
> All-seeing in thy mists, we want no guide,
> Mother of Arrogance, and Source of Pride!

[20] *Ibid.*, IV. 247-254.

We nobly take the high Priori Road,
And reason downward till we doubt of God;
Make Nature still encroach upon his plan;
And shove him off as far as e'er we can:
Thrust some Mechanic Cause into his place;
Or bind in Matter, or diffuse in Space.
Or, at one bound, o'er-leaping all his laws,
Make God Man's Image, Man the final Cause. . . ."[21]

Pope's most devastating response to these tendencies of his time was spoken in those final lines of *The Dunciad*:

See skulking Truth to her old Cavern fled,
Mountains of Casuistry heaped o'er her head!
Philosophy, that lean'd on Heaven before,
Shrinks to her second cause, and is no more.
Physic of Metaphysic begs defence,
And Metaphysic calls for aid on Sense!
See Mystery to Mathematics fly!
In vain! they gaze, turn giddy, rave, and die.
Religion blushing veils her sacred fires,
And unawares Morality expires.
For public Flame, nor private, dares to shine,
Nor human Spark is left, nor Glimpse divine![22]

Such was the climactic protest of the Scriblerians who had begun to speak long before in Swift's *Tale of a Tub* against dangerous tendencies in science, philosophy, and scholarship. They were not opposing "scholarship," "science," or "philosophy"; they were opposing the extremes to which scholarship, science, and philosophy tended to go in the hands of lesser rather than of greater exponents. In their protest against such excesses they were joined by even the "scientific" and "philosophical" poets who elsewhere paid high tribute to

[21] *Ibid.*, IV. 453-478. The "Mechanic Cause" is Descartes'; Hobbes is implied in "bind in Matter"; Newton, probably, in "diffuse in space."
[22] *Ibid.*, IV. 641-652.

[143]

Science! thou fair effusive ray
From the great source of mental Day. . . .
But first with thy resistless light,
Disperse these phantoms from my sight,
   These mimic shades of thee!
The scholiast's learning, sophist's cant,
The visionary bigot's rant,
   The monk's philosophy.[23]

Such general criticism, in which Newton became involved with scientists and philosophers in general, was, however, based largely upon the *Principia*—and that is another story which remains to be told. The *Opticks* had its own metaphysical implications—or, at least as a result of Locke's *Essay*, metaphysical implications were read into it, leading in a different direction, affecting other poets of the period.

II

"So Darkness strikes the sense no less than Light," said Pope. As in its aesthetic theory, so in its metaphysics the supposed Enlightenment seems in retrospect a curious combination of light which illuminated and darkness which blotted out distinction, making all beauty void. In a period when for many men the Cartesian shears had cut matter "out there" from mind "in here," such problems of vision and perception as we have studied were much more poignant than they seem to the intelligent layman today. Plato's man, sitting in his cave, watching the shadows on his walls, becomes a symbol of even the greatest thinkers of the Age of Newton. It was not strange that philosophers like Locke and Berkeley, no less than poets, often drew figures and analogies from the camera obscura, the link between the dark room and the world outside. They watched the reflections upon the walls of their chambers, pondering reality. Locke's famous "closet-simile" takes on added significance when interpreted from this point of view:

[23] Akenside, "Hymn to Science."

Methinks the understanding is not much unlike a closet wholly shut from light, with only some little opening left, to let in external visible resemblances, or ideas of things without: would the pictures coming into a dark room but stay there, and lie so orderly as to be found upon occasion, it would very much resemble the understanding of a man in reference to all objects of sight, and the ideas of them.[24]

Like Descartes and other predecessors, Locke in his dim closet, observing the reflections of external nature through his convex glass, rendered unto Nature those primary qualities whose existence he could not deny, rendered unto the mind of man other qualities which had once been Nature's.

Into Newton his generation and ours have read the same general symbolism, with some justification, to be sure. For Newton who gave color back to the poets and who flooded the world with light, "Newton with his prism and silent face," his "mind forever voyaging on strange seas of thought alone" —he too had darkened his Cambridge room in order that he might see light. "In a very dark Chamber, at a round Hole, about one third Part of an Inch broad, made in the shut of a Window, I placed a Glass Prism, whereby the Beam of the Sun's Light, which came in at that Hole, might be refracted upwards toward the opposite Wall of the Chamber, and there form a colour'd Image of the Sun."[25] "God said, 'Let Newton be,' and all was Light." Outside the sun shone in splendor; but light entered the dark Cambridge chamber only through a pin-prick, light reflected, refracted, inflected.

"It was of the greatest consequence for succeeding thought," writes E. A. Burtt,[26] "that now the great Newton's authority

[24] *Essay Concerning Human Understanding*, Book II, Chapter XI, Section 17. Miss Graham has interpreted this passage in the same way in *Optics and Vision*, p. 96. While the interpretation had occurred to me before I read her book, I realize that I am much indebted to her here and elsewhere.

[25] *Opticks*, Book I, Proposition II, Theorem II; *ed. cit.*, p. 26.

[26] *Metaphysical Foundations of Modern Physical Science*, pp. 236-237.

was squarely behind that view of the cosmos which saw in man a puny, irrelevant spectator (so far as a being wholly imprisoned in a dark room can be called such) of the vast mathematical system whose regular motions according to mechanical principles constituted the world of nature. . . . The world that people had thought themselves living in—a world rich with colour and sound, redolent with fragrance, filled with gladness, love and beauty, speaking everywhere of purposive harmony and creative ideals—was crowded now into minute corners in the brains of scattered organic beings. The really important world outside was a world hard, cold, colourless, silent, and dead; a world of quantity, a world of mathematically computable motions in mechanical regularity." Such was Locke's world; in how far it was Newton's remains conjecture, since Newton sedulously avoided reading ultimate meanings into his own discoveries. Only once in the *Opticks* did he come close to expressing himself on this particular subject, and even then he did not go far:

If at any time I speak of Light and Rays as coloured or endued with Colours, I would be understood to speak not philosophically and properly, but grossly, and accordingly to such Conceptions as vulgar People in seeing all these Experiments would be apt to frame. For the Rays to speak properly are not coloured. In them there is nothing else than a certain Power and Disposition to stir up a Sensation of this or that Colour. . . . Colours in the Object are nothing but a Disposition to reflect this or that sort of Rays more copiously than the rest; in the Rays they are nothing but their Dispositions to propagate this or that Motion into the Sensorium, and in the Sensorium they are Sensations of those Motions under the Forms of Colours.[27]

It is idle to argue the question of the extent to which Newton himself was a subjectivist. His "philosophy" was made

[27] *Opticks*, Book I, Part II, Proposition II, "Definition"; *ed. cit.*, pp. 124-125. In the sentence omitted, Newton uses an analogy between color and sound.

in his own time by philosophers; the world of the eighteenth century, as philosophers now conceive it, was at least unconsciously of his making. "Whatever theory you choose," says Alfred North Whitehead,[28] discussing that world-view, "there is no light or color as a fact in external nature. There is merely motion of material. Again, when the light enters your eyes and falls on the retina, there is merely motion of material. Then your nerves are affected and your brain is affected, and again there is merely motion of material. . . . Nature is a dull affair, soundless, scentless, colourless; merely the hurrying of material, endlessly, meaninglessly. However you disguise it, this is the practical outcome of the characteristic scientific philosophy which closed the seventeenth century." Whence, then, arises that "pleasing delusion" of the beauty of nature, shared by poets and artists for so many hundreds of years? Professor Whitehead replies: "Nature gets credit which should in truth be reserved for ourselves: the rose for its scent; the nightingale for his song; and the sun for his radiance. The poets are entirely mistaken. They should address their lyrics to themselves, and should turn them into odes of self-congratulation on the excellency of the human mind."

So modern critics have reconstructed the world of external nature which the eighteenth century poets should have seen, together with the response which they should have felt toward it and toward themselves. And, indeed, had the poets been philosophers, they might all have seen and felt thus— and poetry would have fallen upon still more evil days. For poets cannot continue to dwell in an abstract world; the school of Pope had carried abstractions as far as was possible. Fortunately for the history of poetry, other spirits were still potent in the land. Fortunately, too, poets are poets and not philosophers. Well as they understood the world-view which the modern philosophers have found in their times, they were capable of believing six impossible (and contradictory) things

[28] *Science and the Modern World*, p. 80.

at once. For one poet who in thoroughgoing fashion imagined the dead world of external nature as scientific philosophy conceived it, there were half a dozen who still continued to live in a world of concrete realities in which there *is* color and scent in the rose, song in the nightingale, and radiance in the sun.

Whether the poets would have grasped the implications of Locke and Newton as fully as they did had it not been for Addison, we can only conjecture. Here, as so often, the essayist stood between philosophers and popular writers, interpreting one group to the other. There is no question that Addison himself realized the ultimate outcome of Descartes *cum* Newton *cum* Locke. In his *Pleasures of the Imagination,* he showed his generation this very picture of external nature:

> Things would make but a poor appearance to the eye, if we saw them only in their proper figures and motions. And what reason can we assign for their exciting in us many of those ideas which are different from anything that exists in the objects themselves (for such are light and colours), were it not to add supernumerary ornaments to the universe, and make it more agreeable to the imagination? We are everywhere entertained with pleasing shows and apparitions, we discover imaginary glories in the heavens, and in the earth, and see some of this visionary beauty poured out over the whole creation; but what a rough and unsightly sketch of Nature should we be entertained with, did all her colouring disappear, and the several distinctions of light and shade vanish?[29]

Addison proceeded to a figure of speech, which, like so many of his figures and analogies, recurred among succeeding popular writers:

> In short, our souls are at present delightfully lost and bewildered in a pleasing delusion, and we walk about like the

[29] This, and the following passages from Addison may be found in *Spectator* 413. Mr. MacLean, in *Locke and English Literature,* p. 94, has considered their relationship to Locke.

[148]

enchanted hero of a romance, who sees beautiful castles, woods, and meadows; and at the same time hears the warbling of birds, and the purling of streams; but upon the finishing of some secret spell, the fantastic scene breaks up, and the disconsolate knight finds himself on a barren heath, or in a solitary desert.

Locke's *Essay* was Addison's specific point of departure; but the extent to which Locke, Newton, and Berkeley[30] were inextricably interwoven is implied in later sentences:

I have here supposed that my reader is acquainted with that great modern discovery, which is at present universally acknowledged by all the inquirers into natural philosophy, namely, that light and colours, as apprehended by the imagination, are only ideas in the mind and not qualities that have any existence in matter. As this is a truth which has been proved incontestably by many modern philosophers, and is indeed one of the finest speculations in that science, if the English reader would see the notion explained at large, he may find it in the eighth chapter of the second book of Mr. Locke's "Essay on Human Understanding."

Edward Young affords the most striking example of a poet who in theory expressed, and in practice carried to ultimate extreme, the implications which critics like Addison in his time and Professors Whitehead and Burtt in ours, have found inherent in the scientific philosophy of the late seventeenth century. Indeed, the *Night Thoughts* might have been written according to their prescription. It was not only the prevailing fashion of "black melancholy" and the "school of night" which dictated the setting of the poem:

> Let Indians, and the gay, like Indians, fond
> Of feather'd fopperies, the sun adore:
> Darkness has more divinity for me;
> It strikes thought inward; it drives back the soul

[30] Berkeley's position seems to be implied in the first sentence below; it is further developed by Young.

To settle on her herself, our point supreme!
There lies our theatre! there sits our judge.
Darkness the curtain drops o'er life's dull scene;
'Tis the kind hand of providence stretcht out,
'Twixt man and vanity; 'tis reason's reign. . . .[31]

Into the camera obscura of perpetual night Young retired in order that Reason, the godlike faculty of man, might see light pure, not discolored, refracted, inflected. There is no color in the world of the *Night Thoughts*; there is only light, the "confluence of ethereal fires From urns unnumber'd" streaming from the steep of heaven. Young's external nature is dark and void of color. His was, indeed, the kind of world which the telescope had showed the moon to be, a world shining only by reflected light, white and dead. Our little earth had become to Young a very small part even of this cosmic universe, and in comparison with the cosmic universes which his imagination conceived, insignificant indeed. Whence, therefore, arose the delusion of man that there is beauty in external nature? Beauty is not in *nature*; it is *man* who confers upon her the beauty which she boasts, man, as the modern critic has suggested, who should reserve for himself the adjectives and epithets he lavishes upon nature, who gives the rose its scent, the nightingale its song, the sun his radiance. All this Young says in verse as categorically as Professor Whitehead says it in prose:

Where thy true treasure? Gold says, "Not in me":
And, "Not in me," the diamond. Gold is poor;
India's insolvent: Seek it in thyself,
Seek in thy naked self, and find it there;
In being so descended, form'd, endow'd; . . .
Erect, immortal, rational, divine![32]

"Reason is man's peculiar; sense, the brute's,"[33] Young always insisted, as he ranged himself in one of the many battles

---

[31] *Night Thoughts*, V. 126-134. [32] *Night Thoughts*, VI. 413-418.
[33] *Ibid.*, VII. 1433.

of the period in which the Lockeans fought to give reason to brutes, the Cartesians to deny it.[34] Yet upon occasion—and this is such an occasion—Young could go further, insisting that man's senses, too, were "divine" as the senses of brutes were not:

> In senses, which inherit earth, and heavens;
> Enjoy the various riches nature yields;
> Far nobler! give the riches they enjoy;
> Give taste to fruits; and harmony to groves;
> Their radiant beams to gold, and gold's bright sire;
> Take in at once the landscape of the world,
> At a small inlet, which a grain might close,
> And half create the wondrous world they see.
> Our senses, as our reason, are divine.
> But for the magic organ's powerful charm,
> Earth were a rude, uncolour'd chaos still.
> Objects are but th' occasion; ours th' exploit;
> Ours is the cloth, the pencil, and the paint,
> Which nature's admirable picture draws;
> And beautifies creation's ample dome. . . .
> Say then, shall man, his thoughts all sent abroad,
> Superior wonders in himself forget,
> His admiration waste on objects round,
> When heaven makes him the soul of all he sees?[35]

At the opposite extreme to Young, both in theory and practice, stood Richard Jago. His long descriptive poem *Edge-Hill* was a paean of praise to the beauty of external nature and to human sight, which enables man to know that beauty.[36] As

[34] Mr. MacLean, *Locke and English Literature*, pp. 71, 80, and *passim*, has shown where Young and other poets stood in this controversy.

[35] *Night Thoughts*, VI. 420-440.

[36] Jago used as a preface to *Edge-Hill* the lines from the *Pleasures of the Imagination*, in which Addison praised sight as the most perfect and delightful of our senses, and the sense basic to the imagination. Jago paused frequently in his long poem to discourse upon sight; he had much to say of both optics and vision. It was he who, in connection with the passage discussed below, retold at length Steele's story of the man born blind, add-

Young in darkness, Jago lived in a world of light and color.
Young was "Il Penseroso" who ponders at night; Jago was
"L'Allegro," delighting to walk briskly "not unseen" over his
native fields and hills in Warwickshire, his eyes constantly
discovering new beauties and dwelling affectionately upon
old familiar ones in nature. With the attitude implied by
Young, Jago had no patience; to think thus is "to quit the
day, And seek our path at midnight." Although he was influenced by both Locke and Newton, he refused to believe that
the understanding is a dark room into which light enters only
through a "hole made in the shut of the window":

> Requires there aught of learning's pompous aid
> To prove that all this outward frame of things
> Is what it seems, not unsubstantial air,
> Ideal vision, or a waking dream,
> Without existence, save what fancy gives?[37]

This is not to say that Jago was unsympathetic to the emphasis of the age upon the "philosophic eye" and the "philosophic
mind"; he was both a "philosophical poet," and a "scientific
versifier." We have already seen him contrasting "the vulgar
race of men" who "on instinct live, not knowing how they
live," with that "sage philosophy" which "explores the cause
Of each phenomenon of sight or sound." He was opposing
not "science" and "philosophy," but certain "metaphysic subtleties," which had been read into science and philosophy:

> Shall we, because we strive in vain to tell
> How matter acts on incorporeal mind,
> Or how, when sleep has lock'd up ev'ry sense,
> Or fevers rage, imagination paints
> Unreal scenes, reject what sober sense

ing material from Molyneux, Locke, Newton, and others conveniently
brought together in one of the treatises on optics standard in his day.

[37] *Edge-Hill*, in Chalmers, XVII. 298. The poem was not published
until 1765, although it is probable that many of the descriptive sections
were written earlier.

And calmest thoughts attest? Shall we confound
States wholly diff'rent? Sleep with wakeful life?
Disease with health? This were to quit the day
And seek our path at midnight. To renounce
Man's surest evidence, and idolize
Imagination. Hence then banish we
These metaphysic subtleties, and mark
The curious structure of these visual orbs,
The windows of the mind; substances how clear,
Aqueous or crystalline! through which the soul
As through a glass, all outward things surveys.[38]

III

Jago, however, belonged to the Age of Hume rather than to
the Age of Locke and Newton, and, influenced by the growing temper of his period, opposed common sense to metaphysics. It is more just to compare Young's response with
that of other poets writing at the same period. Fortunately
an exact comparison can be made, since by a curious coincidence the three most important poems of this period appeared
in the same year. In 1744 when Young produced the complete *Night Thoughts*, Thomson published his revised edition
of *The Seasons*, and Akenside *The Pleasures of Imagination*.
As we have here seen, all three poets were eclectic, and all
three had felt the force of nearly every wind that blew in the
first half of the eighteenth century. Each of them recognized
the power of Locke and expressed admiration for Newton.
All were aware of the implications of both the *Principia* and
the *Opticks*. Both Thomson and Akenside often followed
Locke self-consciously, and there are few major theories of
the *Essay Concerning Human Understanding* which do not,
at one time or another, appear in their poetry.

In the earlier books of *The Pleasures of Imagination*,
Akenside frequently made clear his belief that

[38] *Ibid.*

Mind, Mind alone, bear witness, earth and heav'n,
The living fountains in itself contains
Of beauteous and sublime,[39]

and that Creative Wisdom had given to man, alone among
created beings, not only the ability to understand external
nature, but in his lesser way even to create nature—as Wisdom had created. Much that he implied in his descriptive technique, and expressed in his discussions of the sublime, the
wonderful, the fair in external nature might be construed to
mean that both primary and secondary qualities were in nature herself. In the third book of *The Pleasures of Imagination*, he faced this problem, and after a series of passages
(based on Locke) in which he attempted to show how the
"creative" power of the artist brings order out of a chaos
of impressions, he said:

Perhaps ev'n now some cold, fastidious judge
Casts a disdainful eye; and calls my toil,
And calls the love and beauty which I sing,
The dream of folly. Thou grave censor! say
Is beauty then a dream, because the glooms
Of dullness hang too heavy on thy sense
To let her shine on thee? So the man
Whose eye ne'er open'd on the light of heav'n,
Might smile with scorn while raptur'd vision tells
Of the gay, colour'd radiance flushing bright
O'er all creation. From the wise be far
Such gross, unhallow'd pride; nor needs my song
Descend so low; but rather now unfold,
If human thought could reach, or words unfold,
By what mysterious fabric of the mind,
The deep-felt joys and harmony of sound
Result from airy motion; and from shape
The lovely phantoms of sublime and fair.
By what fine ties hath God connected things

[39] *Pleasures of Imagination*, I. 481-483.

When present in the mind; which in themselves
Have no connection?[40]

Much exists in "nature still indow'd at large," nature which contains "all which life requires," even though she may be "unadorn'd with such inchantment" as man's senses and his fancy and imagination find in her. The primary qualities of matter are hers; the secondary qualities come from the mind of man, "kind illusions" of the creative power which the "source divine of ever-flowing love" and "unmeasur'd goodness" have given him. Although all that is needed to preserve and nourish life is already in nature, God has lavishly added among His gifts the human power to find in the external world more than actually exists in nature:

> Not content
> With every food of life to nourish man,
> By kind illusions of the wond'ring sense
> Thou mak'st all nature beauty to his eye,
> Or music to his ear.[41]

The "philosophic mind" realizes the extent to which certain qualities which seem to make nature beautiful are or are not in nature herself; but it is clear that neither Akenside's Creative Wisdom nor Akenside himself had any blame for the man who loves external nature, even though he may have no awareness that, as he walks abroad, he is in part responsible for creating the secondary qualities in which he delights:

> well-pleas'd he scans
> The goodly prospect; and with inward smiles
> Treads the gay verdure of the painted plain;
> Beholds the azure canopy of heav'n,
> And living lamps that over-arch his head
> With more than regal splendor; bends his ears
> To the full choir of water, air, and earth;
> Nor heeds the pleasing error of his thought,

[40] *Ibid.*, III. 444-464.   [41] *Ibid.*, III. 498-503.

> Nor doubts the painted green or azure arch,
> Nor questions more the music's mingling sounds
> Than space, or motion, or eternal time.[42]

It was quite natural that Akenside, who began *The Pleasures of Imagination* as a versification of Addison's *Pleasures of the Imagination*, should think of man abroad in nature in terms of Addison's enchanted knight:

> So fables tell,
> Th' advent'rous heroe, bound on hard exploits,
> Beholds with glad surprize, by secret spells
> Of some kind sage, the patron of his toils,
> A visionary paradise disclos'd
> Amid the dubious wild: with streams, and shades,
> And airy songs, th' enchanted landscape smiles,
> Chears his long labours, and renews his frame.[43]

Akenside's man is not Thomson's "rude swain," who is constantly contrasted with the man of philosophic mind.[44] Akenside had in mind the intelligent layman, sensitive, responsive, appreciative, yet not necessarily learned in science or philosophy, who responded—as did many an eighteenth century poet—to the beauty of external nature, taking for granted that all the beauty he saw and felt was—as it seems to be—in nature. Akenside was quite correct: such was the attitude of intelligent laymen, who accepted gladly the beauty given by God without entering into metaphysical discussions of the extent to which that beauty was not in nature but was created by the mind of man.

On the whole, such was the attitude of many poets, in part because they were poets, not philosophers, in part because, susceptible though they were to Locke and Newton, they were responding also to many other philosophical winds. The spirit of Plato was abroad in the land in which Locke and

[42] *Ibid.*, III. 493-503. [43] *Ibid.*, III. 507-514.
[44] *Ibid.*, III. 525-535. Akenside too makes use of such a "swain" a few lines further on.

Newton seemed to reign. Akenside suggested his dual allegiance, and his desire to reconcile conflicting trends of thought when he wrote to a friend:

> Lead thou where'er my labor lies,
> And English fancy's eager flame
> To Grecian purity chastize,
> While hand in hand at Wisdom's shrine,
> Beauty with Truth I strive to join,
> And grave assent with glad applause;
> To paint the story of the soul,
> And Plato's visions to control
>   By Verulamian Laws.[45]

The paler yet potent specter of Shaftesbury was hovering over the poets of the mid-century, together with Berkeley and other spirits called from the vastly deep. Like the Olympian gods in an Homeric epic, or the Elements in Milton's Chaos, the shades of Plato with his disciples, Plotinus, Ficino, Pico, the Cambridge Platonists, and Shaftesbury, seemed to "strive here for mastery" over men's souls with the ghosts of Bacon, Descartes, Locke, Newton. Thomson, as so often, exhibited all the tendencies of the period raised to a high degree, the elements so mixed in him that he seemed temporarily to reconcile the irreconcilables.

There are many moments in *The Seasons* when we remember that Thomson wrote in the Age of Newton and Locke, and had developed the characteristic self-consciousness of the period about the processes of vision and perception. Addison had said that the pleasures of the Imagination were "obvious," in comparison with those of Reason: "It is but opening the eye, and the scene enters. The colours paint themselves on the fancy, with very little attention of thought or application of mind in the beholder."[46] As Thomson's "raptured eye hur-

---

[45] "Ode to Caleb Hardinge, M.D.," in *Works*, edited Johnson, Vol. 55, p. 238.
[46] *Spectator* 411.

ries from joy to joy," he seems sometimes only a passive agent "but opening the eye" that the scene might enter. When he writes:

> Or catch thyself the landscape gliding swift
> Athwart imagination's vivid eye,[47]

we recall the camera obscura, which admitted outline, color, motion into the dark-room of the mind. "At night the skies . . . Pour every lustre on the exalted eye"[48]—again man's mind is passive, receiving impressions from the outside world. With the tendency toward analysis characteristic of the period, Thomson followed "Locke, who made the whole internal world his own,"[49] in rendering to each faculty of the soul that which belonged to it, and in watching the mind at work:

> With inward view,
> Thence on the ideal kingdom swift she turns
> Her eye; and instant, at her powerful glance,
> The obedient phantoms vanish or appear;
> Compound, divide, and into order shift,
> Each to his rank, from plain perception up
> To the fair forms of fancy's fleeting train;
> To reason then, deducing truth from truth,
> And notions quite abstract.[50]

By means of Reason man's mind could gain "the heights of science," might soar to "the starry regions or the abyss"; abstracted from the actual scenes of external nature, it might

> wander through the philosophic world,
> Where in bright train continual wonders rise
> Or to the curious or the pious eye.[51]

Yet capable as was Thomson of such abstraction, such searching of heights and depths by means of the "mind's

---

[47] "Spring," ll. 458-459.   [48] "Autumn," ll. 1330-1332.
[49] "Summer," l. 1559.   [50] Ibid., ll. 1788-1796.
[51] "Spring," ll. 923-925.

creative eye," it was not primarily for his Reason and his sage philosophy that his age loved him and we remember him. He was, above all, a poet of imagination, even though his was not yet the "creative imagination" of the Romanticists:

> With swift wing,
> O'er land and sea imagination roams;
> Or truth, divinely breaking on his mind,
> Elates his being.[52]

Walking abroad in nature with eyes that could not choose but see, he "received" sense-impressions which, through the mysterious processes analyzed by Locke and Newton, "affected his fancy" and "furnished his imagination with its ideas." It was fancy which "received"

> The whole magnificence of heaven and earth,
> And every beauty, delicate or bold,
> Obvious or more remote, with livelier sense,
> Diffusive painted on the rapid mind.[53]

"A poet," Addison had said, "should take as much pains in forming his imagination, as a philosopher in cultivating his understanding. He must gain a due relish of the works of nature, and be thoroughly conversant in the various scenery of a country life."[54] Like the critics, the descriptive poets of the Age of Pope assiduously cultivated their gardens of the mind, exposing their imaginations to external impressions, analyzing their responses, developing their "taste" through nature, as critics through books. The "Enthusiast, or Lover of Nature" was born but he was also made. Yet while the poet, a man like other men, was dependent upon his limited senses for the impressions which formed his imagination, as poet he was capable of transcending such limitations. Here again Addison had explained to the poet both the "laws" which governed human perception more rigidly than ever the

---

[52] "Autumn," ll. 1334-1337.   [53] "Summer," ll. 1749-1752.
[54] *Pleasures of the Imagination* (*Spectator* 417).

"rules" governed art, and also the liberty of poets to rise above those laws:

> Words, when well chosen, have so great force in them, that a description often gives us more lively ideas than the sight of things themselves. The reader finds a scene drawn in stronger colours, and painted more to the life in his imagination, with the help of words, than by an actual survey of the scene which they describe. In this case, the poet seems to get the better of nature; he takes, indeed the landscape after her, but gives it more vigorous touches, heightens its beauty, and so enlivens the whole piece, that the images which flow from the objects themselves appear weak and faint, in comparison of those that come from the expressions. The reason, probably, may be, because in the survey of any object we have only so much of it painted on the imagination, as comes in at the eye; but in its description, the poet gives us as free a view of it as he pleases, and discovers to us several parts, that either we did not attend to, or that lay out of our sight when we first beheld it. As we look on any object, our idea of it is, perhaps, made up of two or three simple ideas; but when the poet represents it, he may either give us a more complex idea of it, or only raise in us such ideas as are most apt to affect the imagination.[55]

Such was Thomson's conception of the privilege, and indeed the duty, of a poet. "To me be Nature's volume broad displayed"; often the poet could do no more than "some easy passage, raptured, to translate," but sometimes

> larger prospects of the beauteous whole
> Would gradual open on our opening minds,
> And each diffusive harmony unite
> In full perfection to the astonished eye.[56]

Responsive though he was to the philosophy of Locke and Newton, Thomson never ceased to feel allegiance to the religious and poetical heritage[57] which had preceded his en-

---

[55] *Ibid., Spectator* 416.   [56] "Winter," ll. 579-582.
[57] See particularly Hoxie Neale Fairchild, *Religious Trends in English Poetry, 1700-1740*; Mr. McKillop (*Background of Thomson's Seasons,*

thusiasm for both the philosopher and the scientist, particularly to Shaftesbury and the Neo-Platonic tradition. Different in many ways from his later poetry, his early "Works and Wonders of Almighty Power" expressed in essence the chief theme of *The Seasons*: the glorification of the work of a Deity who had exhibited himself in the Book of God's Works even more than in the Book of God's Word. In *The Seasons* he remembered the *Moralists*, as he had in the early "Works and Wonders."[58] With the Neo-Platonists he felt that "whatever in Nature is beautiful or charming is only the faint shadow of that first beauty."[59] With Shaftesbury he could depart from the classical limitations of his time, seeking beauty in "wild irregularities":

> I shall no longer resist the passion growing in me for things of a natural kind, where neither art nor the conceit or caprice of man has spoiled their genuine order by breaking in upon that primitive state. Even the rude rocks, the mossy caverns, the irregular unwrought grottos and broken falls of waters, with all the horrid graces of the wilderness itself, as representing Nature more, will be the more engaging, and appear with a magnificence beyond the formal mockery of princely gardens.[60]

With Shaftesbury, he could rise to rapture and enthusiasm, finding beauty everywhere in nature which was a creation of Deity:

p. 7), has summed up Mr. Fairchild's conclusions: "In estimating Thomson's relation to science and philosophy we should remind ourselves that he began with a complex of religious and literary motives that has been well described by Professor Fairchild: broad Presbyterianism and the Old Testament, strains of thought from Neo-Platonism and Shaftesbury, the rational ethics of Locke and Addison, enthusiasm for Milton and Virgil, and, we may add, the Longinian theory of the sublime applied to religious poetry. . . ."

[58] See Herbert Drennon, "The Source of Thomson's 'The Works and Wonders of Almighty Power,'" *M.P.*, XXXII (1934), 33-36.

[59] Shaftesbury, *Moralists*, in *Characteristics of Men, Manners, Opinions, Times* . . . , edited J. M. Robertson, London, 1900, II. 126.

[60] *Ibid.*, II. 125.

O glorious Nature! supremely fair, and sovereignly good! all-loving and all-lovely, all-divine! whose looks are so becoming and of such infinite grace; whose study brings such wisdom, and whose contemplation such delight; whose every single work affords an ampler scene, and is a nobler spectacle than all which ever art presented![61]

To Thomson, beauty actually existed in external nature. When he ascended a hill to

> See the country, far-diffus'd around,
> One boundless blush, one white-empurpled shower
> Of mingled blossoms;[62]

when he rejoiced in "This gay profusion of luxurious bliss, This pomp of Nature"[63]; when he described accurately and affectionately the familiar scenes he saw from "thy hill, delightful Shene," or "courting the Muse through Hagley Park," we forget his self-conscious observations of his own perceptions, the momentary remembrances of the camera obscura, the analytic approach of both his "fancy" and his "reason." In spite of his response to Locke and Newton, Thomson never believed himself Addison's "disconsolate knight" on a barren heath or in a solitary desert. His soul was not "lost and bewildered in a pleasant delusion"; to him nature was no "rough unsightly sketch." Intellectually he knew the implications of the metaphysics of Locke and Newton; but emotionally he could not feel that "nature is a dull affair, soundless, scentless, colourless," that "the world that people had thought themselves living in—a world rich with colour and sound, redolent with fragrance, filled with gladness, love, and beauty —was crowded now into minute corners in the brains of scattered inorganic being. The really important world outside was a world hard, cold, colourless, silent, and dead." His "philosophic mind" might soar to the starry regions and the

---

[61] *Ibid.*, II. 98. [62] "Spring," ll. 109-111.
[63] "Summer," ll. 860-861.

abyss, as did Young's: "the radiant tracts on high are her exalted range." But Thomson's brief celestial journeys were not, like Young's, voyages of escape; he was less a "cosmic" than an "excursion" poet; though he, too, soared on the wings of Philosophy, he returned always to this "man-container Earth," secure in the belief that here reality and beauty exist.

Here, then, we find varying reactions of the major eighteenth century poets toward the implications of "Newtonianism," as developed by Locke on the one hand, Berkeley on the other. The "school of Pope" opposed the growing tendency of the time to explain all things scientifically, philosophically, psychologically, opposed the current emphasis upon the mind of man as the measure of all things, the proud belief of the age that man's potentialities were unbounded, and that man by his unaided reason could uncover even the mysteries of God. Others, like Young, followed the metaphysics of the *Opticks* to its ultimate conclusion, seeing in the finite world a dead world, soundless, scentless, colorless, from which they escaped to the empyrean in order to find reality in the "mathematic glories of the skies." Akenside lived in two worlds at once, responding to both. Pope, Young, Akenside were of their period in that they were on the whole abstract poets of thought rather than concrete poets of nature. They were reflecting *ideas* of reality, rather than reality itself. Thomson, in spite of his "science" and "philosophy," was not primarily a scientific or a philosophical poet; he was a poet, in kind the same, if in degree less than Sappho, Sophocles, Shakespeare, Keats, Browning. He too could say:

> you've seen the world,
> The beauty and the wonder and the power,
> The shapes of things, their colour, lights and shades,
> Changes, surprises—and God made all.

The poets of the eighteenth century were conditioned more than they knew by their response to the metaphysics of Locke and Newton, their subconscious acceptance of the dualism of Descartes. The world "out there," the mind "in here," remained to many of them separate and distinct; try as they would, they could not bridge the gap. Even "Imagination," of which they made so much, was unable to go far, "cabin'd, cribb'd, confined, bound in" to one part of man's "soul"; passive rather than active, its place was predetermined, its functions limited. To the school of common sense, the way out of the dilemma seemed simple: let man leave his mental dark-room on the blank walls of which nature was shown only by reflection; let him go forth into the world outside and face reality for himself. The Romanticists went further: nature is not "out there," man "in here"; man and nature are one; man may be wrapt—even lost—in nature. The dislike of the nineteenth century critics for the poets of the eighteenth century, and their critical misunderstanding and even distortion of these earlier writers to whom they categorically denied the proud title, "poet," is comprehensible enough. Conditioned as they were by their Romantic heritage, they were not only repelled by the cleavage between man and nature they felt in the eighteenth century poets but were also offended by the overconsciousness of earlier writers about their intellective processes, which enabled them even in moments of the "Rapture" they so frequently reported, to stand apart from objects of their rapture, observing their own responses, as John Donne, caught in the toils of passion, nevertheless could analyze the psychology of passion. Ironically enough, the very qualities which damned the eighteenth century poets in the eyes of nineteenth century critics have been in part responsible for the present "revival" in which they bid fair to displace those earlier idols of the "intellectual" poets and critics of our time, the "metaphysicals" of the seventeenth century.

EPILOGUE

THE POETIC DAMNATION
OF NEWTON

"O READER, BEHOLD THE PHILOSOPHER'S GRAVE!"[1]

WITH Blake the wheel of fortune will come full-circle. We have seen the Newtonian sun in meridian splendor; we are now to watch the twilight of a god. We have attended Newton in the period of his deification; it is just that we should assist at his damnation. The godlike man who walked the skies is about to be consigned to a circle of Hell deeper than any in Dante; compared with the condemnation of Blake, Keats' stricture at the famous dinner-party was a mere whisper of protest against a Newton who had unweaved the rainbow. If a man is to be judged by his foes no less than by his friends, we may say that the influence of Newton was never better shown than in Blake's violence toward him and all his breed. "Bacon, Locke, Newton"— these were the villains of his pieces; a very special place in his hell was reserved for Newton. Milton was misguided; but the three philosophers were the limbs of Satan, the heirs of iniquity, the "onlie begetters" of all that was vicious and distorted in the thinking of Blake's period. Blake thought he

---

[1] William Blake, "Annotations to Sir Joshua Reynolds' *Discourses*," in *Poetry and Prose of William Blake*, edited Geoffrey Keynes, Bloomsbury, 1927, p. 1003. This section is intended merely as an "epilogue"; it does not pretend to be a thorough study of Blake's "Newtonianism"—a study of much more significance than this easy résumé would indicate. Blake's poetic attitude should be oriented in the anti-Newtonian philosophers of the later eighteenth century. It seemed legitimate, however, to include a short section in Blake merely to show the most extreme reaction against the implications of the *Opticks*.

[165]

hated Newton even more profoundly than the earlier poets had adored him. He never overlooked an occasion for attack upon their idol. Yet we may question whether Blake could have hated Newton so heartily had he not responded to him more than he was willing to admit.

As poet and artist, Blake was immensely susceptible to color: deny it as he might, never did the rainbow shine more fair in his pictures than when seen in connection with the spectrum; his response here was neither that of Noah nor of Thomson's simple swain; yet he said:

> That God is Colouring Newton does shew,
> And the devil is Black outline, all of us know.[2]

But Blake, like the predecessors whom he disavowed, was even more susceptible to light than to color. What he meant by his Frontispiece to *For the Sexes: The Gates of Paradise*, only he knew: here we see infant-man, still involved in a cocoon, eyes closed, about to emerge into reality: Blake's title is, "What is Man?"; his caption,

> The Sun's Light when he unfolds it
> Depends on the Organ that beholds it.[3]

In spite of himself, Blake saw light in terms of Newton's "corpuscles," and though he constantly inveighed against their implications, he coined charming figures from them. To be sure, he read into the "particles of light" ideas which the poetically unimaginative Newton would neither have recognized nor acknowledged. He wrote in a letter to his friend, Thomas Butts, on October 2, 1800:

> To my Friend Butts I write
> My first Vision of Light.
> On the yellow sands sitting.
> The Sun was Emitting
> His Glorious beams,

[2] "To Venetian Artists," *ibid.*, p. 1018.
[3] *Ibid.*, p. 752.

> From Heaven's high Streams. . . .
> The Light of the Morning
> Heaven's Mountains adorning:
> In particles bright
> The jewels of Light
> Distinct shone & clear.
> Amaz'd & in fear
> I each particle gazed,
> Astonish'd, Amaz'd;
> For each was a Man
> Human-form'd. . . .[4]

The Newtonian corpuscles and the Newtonian theories of light are still more clearly seen in the *Book of Los*, in which Blake described the creation of light, its embodiment in the sun, and the subjection of Urizen. For a moment, let us do conscious violence to Blake by considering these lines not as one of his many protests against Newton, but as his heritage from eighteenth century poets who also had responded to Newtonian conceptions of light and ether:

> Then Light first began: from the fires,
> Beams, conducted by fluid so pure,
> Flow'd round the Immense. Los beheld
> Forthwith, writhing upon the dark void,
> The Back bone of Urizen appear
> Hurtling upon the wind
> Like a serpent! like an iron chain
> Whirling about in the Deep. . . .
> And first from those infinite fires,
> The light that flow'd down on the winds
> He siez'd, beating incessant, condensing
> The subtil particles in an Orb.
> Roaring indignant, the bright sparks
> Endur'd the vast Hammer, but unwearied
> Los beat on the Anvil, till glorious
> An immense Orb of fire he fram'd. . . .

[4] "Letters," *ed. cit.*, pp. 1051-1052.

. . . till a Form
Was completed, a Human Illusion
In darkness and deep clouds involv'd.[5]

One more illustration of Blake's use of the Newtonian corpuscles will suffice—again from a poem in which Blake opposed with all his force scoffers and materialists, who like
Bacon, Locke, Newton, Voltaire, Rousseau, denied all that
Blake held holy:

Mock on, Mock on Voltaire, Rousseau:
Mock on, Mock on: 'tis all in vain!
You throw the sand against the wind,
And the wind blows it back again.

And every sand becomes a Gem
Reflected in the beams divine;
Blown back they blind the mocking Eye,
But still in Israel's paths they shine.

The Atoms of Democritus,
And Newton's particles of Light,
Are sands upon the Red sea shore,
Where Israel's tents do shine so bright.[6]

Not even William Blake could have written these three poems
had he not felt the spell of Newton's corpuscles, even though
he opposed the dangers of their implications.

But without any further attempt to suggest that Blake was,
to a greater extent than he realized, "consumed by that which
he was nourished by," let him speak out in vigorous and
vehement language against the implications of the Newtonian
metaphysics, for his invective will serve as a salutary cor-
rective to the excessive adulation we have found in the earlier
period. Blake delighted in nothing more than in his ability to
forge verbal thunderbolts to hurl against Bacon, Locke, and
Newton. He could do it lightly; he could do it seriously. He

[5] *Book of Los*, Chapter IV, *ed. cit.*, pp. 271-272.   [6] *Ed. cit.*, p. 107.

could be pathetic, bathetic, serious, sublime at will; his range, so far as these great adversaries were concerned, was from Lewis Carroll to Isaiah. In one mood he wrote:

> To be, or not to be
> Of great capacity,
> Like Sir Isaac Newton,
> Or Locke, or Doctor South,
> Or Sherlock upon death?
> I'd rather be Sutton.[7]

In "Florentine Ingratitude," he included among satiric verses on Reynolds:

> Ghiotto's Circle or Apelles' Line
> Were not the Work of Sketchers drunk with Wine,
> Nor of the City Clark's warm hearted Fashion,
> Nor of Sir Isaac Newton's Calculation,
> Nor of the City Clark's Idle Facilities
> Which sprang from Sir Isaac Newton's great Abilities.[8]

Even in more pungent verses on the implications of Bacon and Newton, Blake could still take refuge in quips and cranks and wanton wiles, as in these lines on his bête noire, Reynolds:

> Newton & Bacon cry, being badly Nurst:
> "He is all Experiments from last to first.
> He walks & stumbles as if he crep,
> And how high labour'd is every step!"[9]

"My Design in this Book," Newton had written at the beginning of the *Opticks*, "is not to explain the Properties of Light by Hypotheses, but to propose and prove them by Reason and Experiments." To Blake, both "Reason" and "Experiments" were anathema, as were their various exponents, Bacon, Descartes, Locke, and Newton. He thought he hated them all—as no doubt he did. "Art is the Tree of Life," he said in one of his captions to the "Laocoon Group"; "Science

[7] "An Island in the Moon," *ed. cit.*, p. 881.
[8] "Marginalia," *ed. cit.*, p. 1016.   [9] *Ed. cit.*, p. 1018.

[169]

is the Tree of Death."[10] In the "Descriptive Catalogue" of
his exhibition of 1809, he noted in connection with a subject
from Shakespeare's description of Prince Hal: "A Spirit
vaulting from a cloud to turn and wind a fiery Pegasus. . . .
The Horse of Intellect is leaping from the cliffs of Memory
and Reasoning; it is a barren Rock; it is also called the Barren Waste of Locke and Newton."[11] He had written ironically at about the same period:

> You don't believe—I won't attempt to make ye:
> You are asleep—I won't attempt to wake ye.
> Sleep on, Sleep on! while in your pleasant dreams
> Of Reason you may drink of Life's clear streams.
> Reason and Newton, they are quite two things:
> For so the Swallow & the Sparrow sings.
> Reason says "Miracle"; Newton says "Doubt."
> Aye! that's the way to make all Nature out.
> "Doubt, Doubt, & don't believe without experiment."[12]

Newton and Bacon were inextricably involved in Blake's
mind; they were the beginning and the climax of the method
which sought Truth through Experiment. As the supposed
instigator, Bacon was the original villain. "Bacon's Philosophy has Ruin'd England," Blake commented[13]; and again:
"The Great Bacon—he is Call'd; I call him the Little Bacon—
says that Every thing must be done by Experiment; his first
principle is Unbelief."[14] Newton trusted not only in the experimental method, but also in mathematics as an infallible
guide to Truth. "God forbid," said Blake, "that Truth should
be Confined to Mathematical Demonstration"[15]; and, still
more succinctly: "God is not a Mathematical Diagram."[16]

---

[10] *Ed. cit.*, p. 766.
[11] "A Descriptive Catalogue," Number VI, *ed. cit.*, p. 800.
[12] "Epigrams, Verses, and Fragments," *ed. cit.*, p. 845.
[13] "Annotations to Sir Joshua Reynolds' *Discourses*," *ed. cit.*, p. 985.
[14] *Ibid.*, p. 989.
[15] *Ibid.*, p. 1009.
[16] "Annotations to Berkeley's *Siris*," *ed. cit.*, p. 1023.

"The End of Epicurean or Newtonian Philosophy . . . is Atheism."[17]

Among Blake's most sincere reactions to both the aesthetics and metaphysics which earlier poets had read into the Newtonian theories, his marginalia are important for here we catch him off guard; he did not intend these for publication, probably not for any eye save his own. In his "annotations" we may see that the aesthetics which came to a climax in Burke was to Blake a corollary of the metaphysics supposedly engendered by Newton. Blake took exception to various conceptions of the sublime: "Obscurity," he noted abruptly, "is Neither the Source of the Sublime nor of any Thing Else."[18] When Reynolds said that the artist must endeavor to improve mankind "by the grandeur of his ideas" rather than to amuse him by the "minute neatness of his imitations," the artist Blake wrote impatiently: "Without Minute Neatness of Execution The Sublime cannot Exist! Grandeur of Ideas is founded on Precision of Ideas."[19] More violently, he opposed the interpretation of genius which had developed during the eighteenth century, and the tendency of essayists, such as Addison and Burke, to talk vaguely about "Genius" by writing pretty essays on "Taste." Against Reynolds' seventh *Discourse*[20] he noted: "The Purpose of the following discourse is to Prove That Taste & Genius are not of Heavenly Origin & that all who have supposed that they Are so, are to be Consider'd as Weak headed Fanatics." And again: "He who can be bound down is no Genius: Genius cannot be bound."[21] Still more drastic was his comment on another passage in Reynolds: "Bacon's Philosophy has Destroy'd Art & Science. The Man who says that the Genius is not Born but Taught—Is a Knave.

[17] "Annotations to Reynolds' *Discourses*," ed. cit., p. 1010.
[18] *Ibid.*, p. 1007.   [19] *Ibid.*, p. 987.
[20] *Ibid.*, p. 1006.   [21] *Ibid.*

O Reader, behold the Philosopher's Grave!
He was born quite a Fool, but he died quite
a Knave."[22]

In one of his longest passages he combined in his attack the
science and metaphysics of Bacon, Locke, Newton, and the
aesthetics of Burke:

> Burke's Treatise on the Sublime & Beautiful is founded on
> the Opinions of Newton & Locke; on this Treatise Reynolds
> has grounded many of his assertions in all his Discourses. I
> read Burke's Treatise when very Young; at the same time I
> read Locke on Human Understanding & Bacon's Advance-
> ment of Learning; on Every one of these Books I wrote my
> Opinions, & on looking them over find that my Notes on Rey-
> nolds in this Book are exactly Similar. I felt the same Con-
> tempt & Abhorrence then that I do now. They mock Inspira-
> tion & Vision. Inspiration & Vision was then, & now is, & I
> hope will always Remain, my Element, my Eternal Dwelling
> place; how can I then hear it Contemned without returning
> Scorn for Scorn?[23]

Most of all Blake inveighed against that "Philosophy of
Five Senses," which, implied in the empiricism of Bacon, had
been developed, he felt, by Locke's denial of innate ideas and
his emphasis upon experience, which had reached a climax in
Newtonianism and been developed in another direction by
Rousseau. "None could have other than natural or organic
thoughts," Blake wrote in one of his captions to *There Is No
Natural Religion*, "if he had none but organic perceptions."[24]
He said in another of these captions: "Man's perceptions are
not bounded by organs of perception; he perceives more than
sense (tho' ever so acute) can discover."[25] His protest against
the exaltation of the senses as the road to ultimate truth is
heard still more clearly in the song of a fairy in *Europe*:

[22] *Ibid.*, pp. 1002-1003.   [23] *Ibid.*, p. 1011.
[24] *There Is No Natural Religion* (First Series), *ed. cit.*, p. 147.
[25] *Ibid.* (Second Series), p. 148.

Five windows light the cavern'd Man: thro' one he breathes
  the air;
Thro' one hears music of the spheres; thro' one the eternal
  vine
Flourishes that he may receive the grapes; thro' one can look
And see small portions of the eternal world that ever groweth;
Thro' one himself can pass out what time he please; but he
  will not,
For stolen joys are sweet & bread eaten in secret pleasant.[26]

"So sang a Fairy, mocking, as he sat on a streak'd Tulip";
of the fairy the poet asked the question of the eighteenth
century poets: "Then tell me, what is the material world, and
is it dead?"

He laughing, answer'd: "I will write a book on leaves of
  flowers,
If you will feed me on love-thoughts & give me now and then
A cup of sparkling poetic fancies; so, when I am tipsie,
I'll sing to you to this soft lute, and shew you all alive
The world, when every particle of dust breathes forth its joy.

Bacon, Descartes, Locke, Newton—all were earthbound,
perversely denying beauty and reality. In "The Song of Los,"
Blake's was the voice of Isaiah, prophesying doom to their
nation:

Thus the terrible race of Los & Enitharmon gave
Laws & Religions to the sons of Har, binding them more
And more to Earth, closing and restraining,
Till a Philosophy of Five Senses was complete.
Urizen wept & gave it into the hands of Newton and Locke.[27]

Thus the whirligig of time brings in its revenges. To the
poets of the earlier period Newton with his "laws divinely
simple" had brought order out of the chaos of earlier thought,
by showing that the same law which governs the fall of an

[26] *Europe, ed. cit.,* p. 232.
[27] "The Song of Los," *ed. cit.,* p. 274.

apple to the ground also restrains the planets in their courses.
With his prism he had first separated light into colors in his
darkened room; then he had fused the particolored divergent
thought of the age into a single beam of pure light, the light
of Reason, "the Newtonian Sun." Pope wrote the perfect
epitaph for that Newton: "God said, 'Let Newton be!' and
all was Light!" Blake's epitaph was equally succinct: "The
Song of Los is ended. Urizen wept."

INDEX

Addison, Joseph, 7-8, 9, 84, 115, 118, 123, 156, 159-160, 161 n., 162; on camera obscura, 79; and Burke, 123-124; on implications of Newtonianism, 148 ff.
aesthetics, 4-5, 107 ff., 171-172. *See also* Newton
"aether," 36, 42, 48-50, 65, 167
Akenside, Mark, viii, 5, 32-33, 39, 40, 55, 98-99, 107, 108, 123, 130, 133, 144, 163; on "harmony of the senses," 87; on "sublime and beautiful," 117 ff.; on implications of Newtonianism, 153 ff.
Albano, 108
Alberti, Leon Battista, 78
Aldridge, Alfred O., 118 n.
Algarotti, Francesco, 17
Alhazen, 77
Arbuthnot, Dr. John, 8, 60
Aristotle, 76, 92
Atomism, 57, 76, 99-101
Augustine, 37
azure, 44-45

Bacon, Francis, 37, 75, 78, 79, 104, 140, 157, 165, 168, 169, 170, 171, 172, 173
Bacon, Roger, 78
Barrow, Isaac, 6, 7
"Beautiful," 4, 23, 32, 40, 46, 109 ff. *See also* Akenside, Thomson
Behn, Aphra, 17
Berkeley, George, 82, 92, 95, 102, 103, 149, 157, 163, 170 n.
Blackmore, Richard, 57-58, 60, 66-67, 103, 104, 114
Blake, William, 5, 165 ff.
blindness, 82 ff., 129
Boswell, James, 84 n.
Boyle, Robert, 66
Boyse, Samuel, 24, 39
Brooke, Henry, 24, 26, 39, 58, 67-69, 70, 93-94, 101

Browne, Moses, 23, 59, 60
Browne, Sir Thomas, 118
Browning, Robert, 163
Burke, Edmund, viii, 4, 110 n., 123 ff., 171, 172
Burtt, Edwin A., 65 n., 75, 145-146, 149
Butts, Thomas, 166

camera obscura, 77 ff., 94, 144, 158; men of letters on, 78-80
Carew, Thomas, 27
Carroll, Lewis, 169
Carter, Elizabeth, 17
Cassini, Giovanni, 60
Castel, Louis Bernard, 86
Cawthorn, James, 108
Cheyne, Dr. George, 60
"clavecin" or "colour organ," 86
color, interest of popular writers in, 4-8, 14, 23 ff., 35, 36, 71; more exact observation of, 36 ff.; and sound, 65 n., 83-86; and "the beautiful," 110 ff. *See also* Akenside, Thomson
Cunningham, Peter, 114 n.

Dante, 38, 133, 165
darkness, light in, 53-54; and "the sublime," 115 ff.; the "great privation," 127 ff.
Democritus, 76
Derham, William, 16, 57, 59
Desaguliers, J. T., 16, 135-136, 142
Descartes, Réné, 7 n., 22, 37, 73, 77, 82, 91, 93, 94, 103, 143 n., 145, 148, 157, 164, 169, 173
Donne, John, 164
Drennon, Herbert, 3 n., 161 n.

Einstein, Albert, ix
Emery, Clark, viii
epistemology, 89 ff.
ether, *see* "aether"